WITHDRAWN

Nature Into History

NATURE INTO HISTORY

by
LESLIE PAUL

The light, the light, the seeking,
the searching, in chaos, in chaos
—MAORI TEXT

FABER AND FABER LTD

24 Russell Square

London

To Professor H. D. Lewis
of London University

First published in mcmlvii
by Faber and Faber Limited
24 Russell Square London W.C.1
Printed in Great Britain by
Latimer Trend & Co Ltd Plymouth
All rights reserved

Acknowledgements

I wish gratefully to acknowledge my thanks to the publishers, authors and executors whose names follow, for permission to publish extracts from the works listed:
  Messrs. George Allen and Unwin Ltd. for quotation from Oswald Spengler's *Decline of the West* and from Julian Huxley's *Evolution: The Modern Synthesis*. Messrs. Arthur Barker for quotation from Jacques Chegaray's *Bliss in Bali*. Messrs. Jonathan Cape Ltd. for quotation from Carleton S. Coon's *A Reader in General Anthropology* and his *History of Man*, and from Margaret Mead's *Coming of Age in Samoa*. The Syndics of The Cambridge University Press for quotation from Sir Charles Sherrington's *Man on his Nature*. Messrs. Chatto and Windus Ltd. for quotation from Aldous Huxley's *Point Counter Point* and Julian Huxley's *Evolution in Action*. The Chicago University Press for quotation from H. H. Newman's *Evolution, Genetics, Eugenics*. Messrs. Collins Ltd. for quotation from Camara Laye's *The Dark Child*. Messrs. Constable Ltd. for quotation from George Santayana's *The Realm of the Spirit* and from *Reason in Religion* (Vol. 3 of *The Life of Reason*). Messrs. J. M. Dent and Sons Ltd. for quotation from the introduction by W. R. Thompson to the Everyman Edition of Charles Darwin's *Origin of Species*, and from R. A. Wilson's *The Miraculous Birth of Language*. Messrs. Victor Gollancz Ltd. for quotation from Alain Gheerbrant's *The Impossible Adventure*. Messrs. Harper Brothers, New York, for quotation from W. Lloyd

5

ACKNOWLEDGEMENTS

Warner's *A Black Civilisation*. Messrs. Macmillan Ltd. for quotation from Baldwin Spencer and F. J. Gillen's *Northern Tribes of Central Australia* and from the abridged edition of Sir James Frazer's *The Golden Bough*. The Editor of *The Observer* for quotation from an article by L. Harrison Matthews on 'The Bats Retire' in the issue of 11th November 1956. The Oxford University Press for quotation from Isaiah Berlin's *Historical Inevitability*, from R. G. Collingwood's *The Idea of Nature*, and from D. C. Somervell's abridgement of Arnold J. Toynbee's *A Study of History*. Messrs. Penguin Books Ltd. for quotation from Sonia Cole's *The Prehistory of East Africa*, and from Derek Wragge Morley's *The Ant World*. Messrs. Phoenix House Ltd. for quotation from Charles P. Mountford's *Brown Men and Red Sand*. Messrs. Routledge, Kegan Paul Ltd. for quotation from Karl Popper's *The Open Society and Its Enemies*, from Erich Neumann's *Origins and History of Consciousness*, from Bronislaw Malinowski's *The Sexual Life of Savages* and from Sigmund Freud's *Totem and Tabu*. Messrs. Thames and Hudson Ltd. for quotation from E. O. James's *The Nature and Function of Priesthood*. The Trustees of the British Museum for quotation from W. E. le Gros Clark's *History of the Primates*. Messrs. Watts and Co. for quotation from Sir Arthur Keith's *Essays on Human Evolution*. The Yale University Press for quotation from Ellsworth Huntington's *Civilisation and Climate*. The University of California Press for quotation from J. L. Myres' *Who Were the Greeks?*

Contents

Preface

As I concluded this work I read with pleasure an interesting and imaginative account of the birth of art in such caves as those of Altamira and Lascaux by M. Georges Bataille, and was happy to find that he makes there several arguments which are germane to the whole intention of this book. I wish therefore to draw attention to them. He writes that he finds something missing in the investigations made into the life of prehistoric man. He pays tribute, as must we all, since we are so much in their debt, to the anthropologists, ethnologists, sociologists and pre-historians. I certainly owe much to them. Their patient, unsparing, difficult labours have accumulated and classified the data which tell us all we at present know either of the life of primitive men long vanished from the earth or of the nature of contemporary but hardly less primitive cultures. These disciplined labours have brought to a high degree of perfection the study of men in their habitats. This we recognize. 'But', M. Bataille writes, 'obedient to the single method that befits a specialized discipline, they confine their thoughts to reflections upon the evidence at hand: it constitutes their province, and beyond its frontiers they will not venture. Never do they pose in general terms the problem of the transition from animal to man, from twilight to conscious life.'[1]

To study 'the problem of the transition' is the whole purpose of this essay.

[1] *Lascaux or the Birth of Art* ('Prehistoric Painting' in the series 'Great Centuries of Painting'). Text by Georges Bataille. Skira, 1955, p. 30.

9

M. Georges Bataille believes that the scientist has successfully kept out of the difficulty, and that psychology is none too trustworthy in this domain, and that 'the matter is tossed into the lap of the philosophers'. I agree. Whether this is a matter for regret depends on whether you are a philosopher or not. No matter who undertakes it, I consider it highly important to examine the evidence about the primitive state of man in order to discover how precisely it differs from the animal state, and what it is that has brought about the difference.

The 'difference' is no simple matter. M. Bataille believes that in general students of the problem have overlooked one clear distinction between animal and man: 'for an animal nothing is ever forbidden . . . the sociologist and historian of religion focus every time upon particular taboos without first reminding themselves that, generally speaking, human life stripped of prohibitions is unthinkable.'[1]

We see immediately how true this is. Man wraps himself up in codes of morals, manners, styles and magical and religious systems and in social structures which involve at every moment of his life restrictions upon his bodily and mental freedom by which it is inconceivable that an animal should be bound! Man does not simply appear to *find* himself under taboos and prohibitions, he needs them, makes them, seeks them out. The contrast with animal indifference is extraordinary. Yet what is so true in this field of moral and social laws, no longer operates when we move into the technical and economic fields. Here the picture is reversed. It is the animal which is fast bound, and man who is completely free. There is no ban on the limits to which man can go technically. In general this seems to have been true from earliest times. No prohibitions or taboos have ever effectively stood in the way of his increasing mastery of nature, his inventiveness, his discovery of new sources of energy or his conservation of old. There has been a steady improvement in man's technical skill right up to the last century, since when progress has become a frenzy. With some slight modification much the same might be said about

[1] Ibid., p. 31.

man's accumulation of scientific knowledge. Nothing like it exists on the animal side. No lions develop antelope farms to ensure a steady supply of meat and to expand the lion kingdom in deference to an imperial urge, regal though the beast is. Nor do we find the hungry giraffe embarking on tree planting. The animal which is free to follow its natural impulses, is nevertheless caught fast within them. This is true even in the insect kingdoms of ant and bee where we find some resemblance to human economies. The insect economies are fast frozen. Man, who wraps himself in prohibitions in one sphere, is completely free of them in another! The enigma may be solved if we assume that both in their different ways constitute a rejection of the animal situation. It is perhaps significant here that M. Bataille, like others before him of course, discovers that prehistoric artists shrank from painting man with the realism which they brought to the portrayal of the beasts they hunted. In cave art, man is almost always in some disguise. That which the artist saw in the beasts he seems to have refused to acknowledge in himself. It seems 'almost to imply a systematic effort to preserve man from naturalism'. No equivalent concern bothers an animal. It does not even 'see itself' as the human does, let alone contrast itself with the human condition.

Let me say then that these are the themes which I seek to explore in the pages which follow. Is history simply a continuation of evolution? Is man just a beast writ large, with somewhat stronger but in no sense different equipment from the animal? If we answer *yes* to both these questions, what account do we give of human activities which appear to be non-beastlike? If we answer *no*, then what too does *that* imply? This therefore is one of those frontier studies upon which I found myself launched almost against my will, not simply out of a need to understand man as clearly as possible, but in order to defend him from the ludicrous over-simplification of his nature, status and needs to which a century of sentimental evolutionary thinking has reduced him.

Brasted Place, February 1957   **L. P.**

CHAPTER 1

History and Evolution

In the last century most intelligent men came to believe that they knew pretty well what history was about and where it was going. And although there were many great and important differences between the schools of, for instance, Hegel and Comte and Spencer and (in this century) Spengler, yet what strikes the critic now is not so much how they differed, but how much they agreed. Whether it was the Hegelian thesis of history as the Unfolding Idea or Absolute, or the Spencerian notion of an inevitable evolution towards human perfection, or the humanistic philosophy of Auguste Comte who believed that mankind had moved from religion to philosophy and was finally to come to grips with reality through science, or whether it was simply the liberal and humanist idea of a beneficent but irresistible human progress, the general inspiration was clear enough. History was moving mankind onwards towards some ascertainable earthly goal. History, like nature, was obedient to laws. As and when they were discovered the future could be predicted. Progress was one of the laws, though opinions might differ as to what progress was. Even Lord Acton, Regius Professor of History at Cambridge, the Roman Catholic, who ought to have known better, was able to say out of the rosy optimism of his times that 'this constancy of progress, of progress in the direction of organised and assured freedom, is the characteristic fact of modern history, and its tribute to the theory of Providence,'[1] and he quoted the bold declaration of Herschel that, 'in whatever state of knowledge we may conceive man to be placed, his progress towards a yet higher state need never fear a check, but must continue until the last existence of society.' And Darwin, too, manifestly against the very argument of the struggle for existence, was blithely able to assert that 'as natural selection works solely by and for the good of each being, all corporeal and mental endowments will tend to progress towards perfection.' The theory of progress consoled John Stuart Mill with the expectation that all the grand sources of human suffering would be presently removed by human care and effort, which led me to remark some years ago, in *The Meaning of Human Existence*, that human care and effort were themselves sources of suffering.

Nineteenth-century hopes transmitted to this century such an infectious *mystique* of progress that H. G. Wells virtually threw away the comic genius which gave us Mr. Polly and Kipps and Ponderevo and Bealby in order to preach that in a world where history and evolution were one process, 'Can we doubt that presently our race will more than realise our boldest imaginations, that it will achieve unity and peace, that it will live, the children of our blood and lives will live, in a world made more splendid and lovely than any palace or garden that we know, going on from strength to strength in an ever-widening circle of adventure and achievement? What man has done, the little triumphs of his present state . . . form but the prelude to the things that man has yet to do.'[2]

The notion that human history was 'a record of progress—a record of accumulating knowledge and increasing wisdom, of continual advancement from a lower to a higher platform of intelligence and wellbeing . . .' under 'the beneficent regulation of great providential laws'[3] dies hard. Julian Huxley writing in 1940 in the midst of the Second World War of the century when

---

[1] *The Study of History*, London 1911, p. 28.

[2] The last paragraph of *A Short History of the World*, 1934 Edn.

[3] *The Nineteenth Century—A History*, R. Mackenzie, 1880. From Collingwood, *Idea of History*, 1946, p. 146.

it seemed doubtful whether Western Civilization could survive, looked hopefully at both Communism and National Socialism and saw in them Comtean portents of the end of the age of superstition and the beginning of religions of humanity![1] It must have taken the most starry-eyed idealism to see in the mid-century manifestations of those savage movements a real human advance! Yet Marxists also, of course, have always clung to the same idealism about progress and used the coming of the golden age to justify the terror they practised. Marx and Engels turned their backs most pointedly upon all the mild-mannered prophets of a kindly progress they encountered, and could not be sufficiently rude to them; but they did not turn their backs on progress: they simply believed it to be bloody as well as inexorable. However, the end was just the same—a triumphant entry into the golden age, belief in which caused the hard-headed Lenin to write that 'only then [after the victory of the proletariat] will be possible and will be realized a really full democracy, a democracy without exceptions. Only then will democracy itself wither away in virtue of the simple fact that, freed from capitalist slavery, from the innumerable horrors, savagery, absurdities and infamies of capitalist exploitation, people will gradually become accustomed to the observation of the elementary rules of social life, known for centuries, repeated for thousands of years in all sermons. They will become accustomed to their observance without force, without constraint, without subjection, without the special apparatus for compulsion which was called the state.'[2]

If we turn to Nietzsche, it is not by any manner of means a liberal doctrine of progress which we find in his pages, but it certainly is in some sort an evolutionary one. Man is still made to be surpassed—by Superman. Nietzsche turned nineteenth-century bourgeois morality on its head, and all that which for

[1] *See* Julian Huxley's 1940 (!) preface to Thinkers' Library Edition of *Religion Without Revelation* in which he says that 'social movements of a religious nature' such as Communism and Nazism, 'taking the place of traditional theological religion' were 'a symptom and a portent of the rise of humanist religions'.

[2] *The State and Revolution*, 1917.

it was virtue became vice for him. 'That virtue which Schopenhauer still proclaimed as superior to all, and as the most fundamental of all virtues; even that same pity I recognized as more dangerous than any vice. Deliberately to thwart the law of selection among species, and their natural means of purging their stock of degenerate members—this, up to my time, had been the greatest of all virtues. . . ' And out of the tramplings and scourgings and dark conflicts which he predicted, out of an endless nihilistic struggle for power, would come the period of catastrophe which would sift mankind, for 'Man is a shame and disgrace and should be transcended'.

In Spengler, on the other hand, nature and history become one, for the law of the natural cycle covers them both, and what future a human Leviathan possesses can be predicted from the stage one decides it has reached in its natural cycle. ' "Mankind",' exclaims Spengler, with all the exuberance of a Carlyle, "is a zoological expression, or an empty word. But conjure away the phantom, break the magic circle, and at once there emerges an astonishing wealth of *actual* forms—the Living with all its immense fullness, depth and movement—hitherto veiled by a catchword, a dryasdust scheme, and a set of personal "ideals". I see, in place of that empty figment of *one* linear history which can only be kept up by shutting one's eyes to the overwhelming multitude of the facts, the drama of *a number* of mighty Cultures, each springing with primitive strength from the soil of a mother-region to which it remains firmly bound throughout its whole life-cycle; each stamping its material, its mankind in *its own* image; each having *its own* idea, *its own* passions, *its own* life, will and feeling, *its own* death. Here indeed are colours, lights, movements, that no intellectual eye has yet discovered. Here the Cultures, peoples, languages, truths, gods, landscapes bloom and age as the oaks and the stone-pines, the blossoms, twigs and leaves—but there is no ageing "Mankind". Each Culture has its own new possibilities of self-expression which arise, ripen, decay, and never return.'[1]

In our day, under the impact of many political and scientific

[1] *The Decline of the West*, Spengler, London, undated, p. 21.

shocks, and military and civil crimes committed in the name of progress, which have given man a nausea for the heady and gaseous philosophical theories of the last century, all this kind of stuff is being jettisoned. The laws and certainties of our fore-fathers are being taken out of history—and out of nature too, for that matter. And the professional historian looks as askance today at Professor Toynbee and his theories of the dynamics of civilization as once historians looked down their noses at the efforts of H. G. Wells to write that story of mankind they them-selves had shirked.

The breathless polemic which Dr. Isaiah Berlin recently launched against all preachers of Historical Inevitability is a splendid sample of the new attack. Theories of historical in-evitability rest, Dr. Berlin wrote, 'on the belief that everything is caused to appear as it does by the machinery of history itself— by the impersonal forces of class, race, culture, History, the Life-Force, Progress, The Spirit of the Age. Given this organiza-tion of our lives which we did not create and cannot alter, it, and it alone is ultimately responsible for everything. To blame or praise individuals or groups of individuals for acting rightly or wrongly, so far as this entails a suggestion that they are in some sense genuinely free to choose between alternatives, and may therefore be justly and reasonably blamed or praised for choos-ing as they did and do, is a vast blunder, a return to some primitive or naïve conception of human beings as being able somehow to evade total control of their lives by forces natural or supernatural, a relapse into childish animism which the study of any scientific or metaphysical system should swiftly dispel. For if such choices were real, the determined world structure which alone, on this view, makes possible complete explanation, whether scientific or metaphysical, could not ex-ist. And this is ruled out as unthinkable; "reason rejects it"; it is confused, delusive, superficial, a piece of puerile megalomania, pre-scientific, unworthy of civilised men.'[1]

[1] *Historical Inevitability*, London, 1954, pp. 12-13. We note the irony of the fact that this was the 'Auguste Comte Memorial Lecture, No. 1'. For a less uncompromising view of the rôle of the modern historian *see* Geoffrey Barraclough's *History in a Changing World*, Oxford, 1955.

Dr. Berlin goes on, effortlessly sardonic, to demonstrate how the prestige of natural science spurred on the historians to subsume their studies under scientific laws. But this futile and dangerous effort has been made in the service, he claims, of an imaginary science the preachers of which, 'like the astrologers and magicians whom they have succeeded, cast up their eyes into the clouds, and speak in immense, unsubstantiated images and similes, in deeply misleading metaphors and allegories, and make use of hypnotic formulae with little regard for experience, or rational argument, or tests of proven reliability. Thereby they throw dust in their own eyes as well as ours, obstruct our vision of the real world, and further confuse an already sufficiently bewildered public about the relations of value to fact, and, even more, the nature and methods of the natural sciences and historical studies.'[1]

The humble and tentative approach to the enigmas of history, to

> *All that man is,*
> *All mere complexities,*
> *The fury and the mire of human veins*

which this new mood has given birth to, is altogether admirable, and we cannot be too thankful for it. Yet it seems to me still insecurely based. It lacks, or it seems to me that it lacks, a clear sense of what history is, and is about, and the most urgent historical task is to make this plain, especially if we accept, as I myself do, the dictum of Collingwood that history must play a liberating rôle for our times and help us to escape the intellectual imprisonment contrived by science between 1600 and 1900. The new mood of which Dr. Berlin is specially representative is part Christian, part humanist, I suppose. It treats man as given, and history as the mirror of his human condition, and it refuses to go further than that, either to the deduction of general historical laws, or to the creation of official systems on the Marxist or Hegelian scale, or to the imprisonment of history within 'natural history'. Well and good! But then, in that

[1] *Historical Inevitability*, pp. 78-9.

case, *what is the relation of history to evolution?* This is something which cannot be burked. The evolutionists are sure that history is a continuation of evolution, and so are some historians, for they are sure that man is an evolving animal. And that is as much as to assert that there must be an evolutionary thread linking all history whether we are capable of discerning it or not. Those who are sceptical may refuse to expose the evolutionary laws in history, either because they cannot find them at all, or because the evidence is insufficient. But men are always moved by grand simplifications, and evolution is such, historically speaking, and they will relate evolution and history even in the absence of evidence, unless they are shown reasons why they should not. Indeed, the obvious intellectual necessity to speak of the relation between them will compel many men, whether historians or not, to claim the right to do so, and in doing so to render the whole content of history once again a mine in which the heady speculator and scientific impostor will dig for ore. Men are bound to go on asking to be told the significance of human history, and if the historian cannot tell them, they will turn to the evolutionary propagandist, to the *mystique*-maker, or to the Marxist to do so for them.

The command to go on to determine the nature of history is all the stronger just because the climate of our times is still, despite the present revolt of the historians, very much dominated intellectually by the 'developmental thesis' of Herbert Spencer, by the notion, in other words, of unbroken organic continuity up to and including human history. For the intellectual of the first half of this century evolution constituted a moral and physical challenge of the kind which Mark Rampion speaks about in his conversation with Burlap in Aldous Huxley's *Point Counter Point*. Mark Rampion (a portrait of D. H. Lawrence) managed to combine defence of natural man and of evolution with condemnation of learning:

' "The lizards died of having too much body and too little head," said Rampion in explanation. "So at least the scientists are never tired of telling us. Physical size is a handicap after a certain point. But what about mental size? These fools seem to

forget that they're just as top-heavy and clumsy and dis-
proportioned as any diplodocus. Sacrificing physical life and
affective life to mental life. What do they imagine's going to
happen?"

'Burlap nodded his agreement. "That's what I've always
asked. Man can't live without a heart."

' "Not to mention bowels and skin and bones and flesh," said
Rampion. "They're just marching towards extinction. And a
damned good thing too. Only the trouble is that they're marching the rest of the world along with them. Blast their eyes! I
must say, I resent being condemned to extinction because these
imbeciles of scientists and moralists and spiritualists and tech-
nicians and literary and political uplifters and all the rest of
them haven't the sense to see that man must live as a man, not
as a monster of conscious braininess and soulfulness. Grr! I'd
like to kill the lot of them." '[1]

After this violent and vulgar expression of opinion Rampion
shows Burlap two drawings representing alternative views of
the evolutionary process. The one, which purports to be The
Outline of History according to H. G. Wells, shows an evolutionary procession beginning with quite tiny monkeys which
grow into ever larger and mightier beings until mankind
comes to a contemporary consummation in the figures of Mr.
H. G. Wells and Sir Alfred Mond. The procession trails away
towards a Utopian infinity, with Wells and Mond 'growing
larger and larger at every repetition'. The other drawing em-
bodies Rampion's caustic criticism of the products of evolution.
Bronze-age man was a good size, the Greek even larger, the
Roman small again, and the monks of the Thebaid, 'primeval
little monkeys'. Robust, earthy Florentines, English and
French were large-scale beings, but Calvin, Knox, Baxter and
Wesley 'revolting monsters'. From twentieth-century abortions
of humanity, the future faded into a mess of gargoyles and
foetuses with 'the tails of apes and the faces of our most eminent
contemporaries' engaged in furious and destructive conflict.

Of course, Rampion's coarse evolutionary arguments mask

[1] Op. cit., London, 1928, pp. 289-90.

HISTORY AND EVOLUTION

an angry social criticism, particularly of that complacent, liberal doctrine of progress which I have already examined which assumes that somehow every new generation is better than the previous one. In this Rampion is the instrument of his creator's acute and disgusted mind. We are compelled to recognize in *Point Counter Point* the great and significant novel of 'evolutionary' humanity. It is the 'agonizing reappraisal' of the Great War generation of man's helpless animality in the light not only of evolution but of war and social disaster. And its theme is despair that the cell becomes a worm, the worm becomes a fish, the fish turns into the foetus of a mammal and the mammal becomes the boy who in fifteen years' time gets confirmed by an unctuous Bishop into a sick humanity. The conclusion really is, or so I read it, that evolutionary extinction is better than the continuation of human sexual rottenness.

This is very much the same kind of thing as Conrad says in *Back to Methuselah*, (that first effort to produce what Shaw called the Bible of Creative Evolution)—'The power my brother calls God proceeds by the method of Trial and Error; and if we turn out to be one of the errors, we shall go the way of the mastodon and megatherium and all other scrapped experiments.'

When I myself wrote my first novel[1] early in the thirties I was determined to introduce the same theme for it seemed to me that the first thing about which a young man ought to make up his mind was the evolutionary ruthlessness of life. And so I made one of my characters describe men as 'a biological accident. Why should we worry about them? Pity and sympathy, keeping the sick alive, letting the feeble-minded breed—all damned absurdity, don't you think? It's a process of perpetuating the weak at the expense of the strong. We ought to preach the gospel of the strong.' And if all this kind of nonsense tended to shade over into a Shavian religion of evolution as the path to the Godhead—'A man differs from a microbe only in being farther along that path'—we ought not to forget the deadly seriousness behind it.

[1] *Fugitive Morning*, 1932.

The thirties are not the fifties, but evolutionary theories applied to man and his history do not lack their exponents still. In the last chapter of *Evolution: The Modern Synthesis* Julian Huxley sums up his biological findings and defends evolutionary progress in the human context. The last step in evolution, he says, has been the coming of 'the degree of intelligence which involves true speech and conceptual thought: and it is found exclusively in man.' If man were wiped out, Dr. Huxley writes, 'it is in the highest degree improbable that the step to conceptual thought would be taken again, even by his nearest kin.'[1] What is more remarkable is his assertion that 'Only along one single line is progress and its future possibility being continued —the line of man.'[2] Elsewhere, evolutionary progress appears to have come to a halt in a series of blind alleys. The advance of the 'echinoderms for instance reached its climax before the end of the Mesozoic. For the arthropods, represented by their highest group, the insects, the full stop seems to have come in the early Cenozoic: even the ants and bees have made no advance since the Oligocene. For the birds, the Miocene marked the end: for the mammals, the Pliocene.'[3] Only man therefore is left. But, says Huxley, in considering human evolution we have to take into account human values—that man can through his mind reach conclusions about what he wants and how he is going to get it, and this must form therefore a factor in *his* evolution, and a new factor in evolution altogether. 'The future of progressive evolution is the future of man. The future of man, if it is to be a progress and not merely a standstill or degeneration, must be guided by a deliberate purpose'[4] ... 'True human progress consists in increases of aesthetic, intellectual, and spiritual experience and satisfaction.'[5] 'The evolutionary biologist is tempted to ask whether the aim should not

[1] *Evolution: The Modern Synthesis*, London, 1942, p. 571.
[2] Ibid.
[3] Ibid.
[4] Ibid., p. 577. *See also* Julian Huxley's *The Uniqueness of Man*, London, 1941, and *Evolution as a Process*, ed. by Julian Huxley, A. C. Hardy, E. B. Ford, London, 1954.
[5] Ibid., pp. 575-6.

be to let the mammal die within us, so as the more effectually to permit the man to live.'[1]

However, though Huxley recognizes that evolution finally becomes merged into the whole system of human values, he does not really suppose, if I understand him, that the human values should be the standard by which the validity of the evolutionary hypothesis, and the morality of the evolutionary process, are themselves to be judged. Nor does he argue on the side of his grandfather that human values must struggle against cosmic processes if these turn out to be opposed to them—but rather the contrary, that evolution itself remains the yardstick by which human values are to be judged and it is impious to suppose otherwise. In *On Living in a Revolution* he rebuked his grandfather for imagining that human moral standards had any absolute value, and protested that he could not understand how anyone could suppose that it was man's duty to fight against the process which had brought him to birth. In *Evolution in Action* he announced that he was attempting to rethink human life *sub specie evolutionis* and he said this: 'The biologist knows how fruitful has been the study of the mechanism of genetic transmission for understanding the process of biological evolution. He can properly suggest to the humanist that a study of the mechanism of cultural transmission will be equally fruitful for understanding the process of human history. Ideas, rituals, symbols, transmissible skills, beliefs, works of art—these seem to be the chief vehicles of this transmission. In addition to the self-reproduction and self-variation of material substance, in the shape of genes, we have now to consider the self-reproduction and self-variation of mental activities, operating through the various media of cultural inheritance. . .'[2] He believes too that 'there are standards in human evolution. One school of anthropologists is never tired of proclaiming the doctrines of cultural relativity—that different cultures are not higher nor lower, but merely adjusted in different ways. But this is to neglect the lessons of biology. To take an extreme example, no biologist doubts that the spiny ant-eater is a survivor of the primitive

[1] Ibid.   [2] Op. cit., London, 1953, p. 135.

proto-mammalian type, although we can be sure that none of the original proto-mammals had long prickly spines and a specialized ant-eating mouth and tongue. In the same way, I should say there can be no doubt that the social and cultural organization of the Australian black-fellows is a survival of a very low and primitive type of culture, even though some features of it, like the intricate details of its totems and its marriage system, are clearly a recent specialization.'[1]

We are compelled to recognize in all this, the latest development of that doctrine which J. B. Bury pronounced some half a century ago that 'the diffusion of the Darwinian theory of the origin of man, by emphasizing the idea of continuity and breaking down the barriers between human and animal kingdoms, has had an important effect in establishing the position of history among the sciences which deal with telluric development. The perspective of history is merged in a larger perspective of development. As one of the objects of biology is to find the exact steps in the genealogy of man from the lowest organic form, so the scope of history is to determine the stages in the unique causal series from the most rudimentary to the present state of human civilisation.'[2]

We might fruitfully compare these arguments about human evolution with those which Sir Arthur Keith advanced in *Essays on Human Evolution* (1946). In it he argued for the existence of a double human code. In one aspect of his nature, that which led him into hostility against, and war with, his 'enemy', man was on the side of that cosmical code which T. H. Huxley condemned and Julian Huxley praised; in another aspect of his nature man was moved by that ethical code which brought him to love his neighbour and to deal justly and compassionately with him. Both codes were necessary to evolution, for the second made possible the existence of organized human societies while the first ensured that the societies remained distinct from

[1] Ibid., pp. 139-40.
[2] *Darwin and Modern Science*. Commemorative essays. Edited by A. C. Seward, Cambridge, 1909. Essay XXVII, Darwinism and History, J. B. Bury, p. 535.

one another and engaged in a corporate struggle for existence with one another. The preaching of this doctrine, with its argument that 'war is nature's pruning hook', involved Sir Arthur in much controversy.

He developed his general argument thus: 'Tribalism was Nature's method in bringing about the evolution of man. I have already explained what a tribe really is—a corporation of human beings entrusted with a certain capital of genes. The business of such a corporation is to nurse and develop its stock of genes—to bring them to an evolutionary fruition. To reach such an end a tribal corporation had to comply with two conditions—(1) it had to endure for a long age; (2) it had to remain intact and separate from all neighbouring and competing tribes. Human nature was fashioned or evolved just to secure these two conditions—continuity through time and separation in space. . . What then, is the explanation which the student of human evolution has to offer as a final purpose for Man's existence? It is not, as the Victorian scientists thought, to permit the individual man or woman to develop their latent potentialities; but to permit a closed society, be it tribe or nation, to develop its collective potentialities of brain and of body as an evolutionary unit.'[1]

The first point of interest which emerges from these quotations is that in all of them human history is assumed, *absolutely without question*, to be a continuation of evolution: but the second point which we derive from Julian Huxley is perhaps of more importance at the moment—that evolution appears to have come to a blind alley, biologically speaking. There is no evidence apparently that organic advance is going on still, and so what remains of evolution is human history! If we want therefore to speak of evolution at all as a continuing process we have to talk of it solely in terms of man, or rather of his highest human qualities, those which precisely distinguish him from the animal, and we have no reason to expect that the human activities which spring from them will affect man's physical inheritance

---

[1] *Essays on Human Evolution*, Sir Arthur Keith, 1946, p. 23.

one way or the other. But the aesthetic, intellectual and spiritual qualities of which Julian Huxley speaks as the present instruments of evolution are precisely those which man is incapable of satisfying by his natural inheritance. He can only express them through the forms of social, political, religious, aesthetic and moral life. And all the corporate instruments through which man gives expression to these aspects of his life are creations of men and not endowments of nature. The spring dress of the mallard drake, the tail of the peacock, the song of the nightingale are not really to be compared with the costume of a Balinese dancer, the robes of a priest, the anthem of a church choir. For the one set are natural endowments which no individual organism can alter: the other have to be entirely created by men out of nothing.

If therefore evolution is now to be judged by this inward creative power of man, a power which enables him to live by artifice and against nature, we must not only say that evolution has come to an end biologically, but that it has been transformed in human history into something as unlike that from which it sprang as cheese is unlike chalk. What then is the point of using the term 'evolution' in connection with man's life? Could we not say that for man the Pleistocene 'marked the end'? Indeed, leaving aside the possibility that evolution, if it really took place as we are told it did, is an exhausted force, the break between a biological evolution and a spiritual history is so great that nothing but the presence of a fashionable *mystique* about evolution could persuade us to speak of the two as aspects of the same natural process. Philip Fothergill has pointed out that much of the confusion and bitterness which has surrounded the Darwinian controversy sprang from the fact that Darwinian concepts were married to a general philosophy of evolution, and were used to support or even to 'prove' the validity of materialistic and mechanistic theories about the cosmic process.[1] The Piltdown skull exposure suggests that it generated in some minds a desire to forge the evidence where it did not exist.

Yet we really cannot compare the fashionable contemporary

[1] *Historical Aspects of Organic Evolution*, London, 1952, esp. p. 346.

mystique with the heroic if forgotten efforts of Spencer and even A. N. Whitehead to bring all Process under a strenuous intellectual scrutiny and to deduce from it great metaphysical principles. The evolutionary idea today is too often simply an unexamined preconception of the kind which caused Sir Charles Sherrington to write not long ago in *Man on his Nature*: 'Our world we recognize today as a world in the making, and ourselves as part of it likewise in the course of making. Our present is not only not static, its very motion is a motion which will tomorrow not repeat today. Our planetary islet is unfinished even as those island universes which the astronomer tells us are at various stages of becoming. Kant seems to assume the human mind to be a finished thing... But the human mind is part of a tide of change which, in its instance, has been latterly and, we may think, still is, running like a mill-race. Living things are all the time busy becoming something other than what they are. And this, our mind, with the rest. It is being made along with our planet's making. We do not know that it will ever be finished.'[1]

That passage very richly illuminates the sentimental philosophy of evolutionary continuity which dreams of a perpetual flux of forms, sees living creatures engaging in an everlasting General Post, and nothing whatever what it is supposed to be, and everything what it is not.

In the face of such nonsense—all of a piece with that which Dr. Berlin castigates—a certain urgency does attach to the effort to separate what is true from what is false in the evolutionary idea as applied to man. Perhaps it is also imperative today to separate what is true from what is false in the evolutionary idea itself. The notion of the evolution of species is, in itself, a useful hypothesis. It is the only theory which seems to introduce order into a great deal of the evidence. What Dr. H. H. Newman wrote in 1935 has much common sense to support it: 'The nature of the proof of organic evolution, then, is this: that, using the concept of organic evolution as a working hypothesis, it has been possible to rationalize and render intelligible, a vast

[1] *Man on his Nature*, Cambridge, 1940, pp. 168-9.

array of observed phenomena, the real facts upon which evolution rests. Thus, classification (taxonomy), comparative anatomy, genetics become consistent and orderly sciences when based on evolutionary foundations, and when viewed in any other way they are thrust into the utmost confusion. There is no [other] generalization known to man which is of the least value in giving these bodies of facts any sort of coherence and unity. In other words, the working hypothesis works, and is therefore acceptable as truth until overthrown by a more workable hypothesis.'[1]

Yet that very passage, sensible as it is in many ways, reveals the whole difficulty of the evolutionary case. The fact that a working hypothesis works does not establish that it is finally true: it merely establishes that it works. Theories about the ether popular fifty years ago were hypotheses to explain certain facts: they 'worked', they 'explained' why light behaved as it did, but in their very nature could not be proved true. The theories of the structure and dynamism of the unconscious advanced by Freud are hypotheses which seem to work, but the fact that they fit what is so far known, does not prove them to be true. Indeed, in the first two studies mentioned by Dr. Newman he is clearly thinking of evolutionary theory as a useful classificatory device: the genealogical arrangement of forms of known organisms simplifies these studies in an aesthetically pleasing way. Anatomically, by way of the theory, forms can be arranged in a pattern leading from the most simple to the most complex. But such an arrangement does not prove that the more complex form developed from the more simple form. The arrangement of the evidence might favour such a conclusion, but would not in itself prove such a development to have taken place. One sees this immediately by transferring the argument to motor-cars. It is possible to arrange a table or tree showing the development of advanced types of cars from the more primitive kinds. I saw such an argument used in a picture book on evolution written by an admiral. But in fact there is no generation of one car by another: what might appear to an in-

[1] *Evolution, Genetics, Eugenics*, 1935, p. 51.

vestigating Martian as proof of generation of the complex from the simple is, we know, proof only that one design is discarded by an independent designer and a new substituted. The car itself has nothing to do with the process. The notion of an independent intelligent designer at work on living material is not however one which has found favour with evolutionists. And it must be urged that the logical order is not necessarily the natural order—which is the mistake which empiricists continually make—nor, again, is the aesthetically most pleasing order necessarily the true one. It is, indeed, intellectually satisfactory to derive all complex forms from simpler ones and to assume therefore a general drive in nature towards this end: but it is difficult to reconcile this with the co-existence *at this present moment* of myriads of forms of every degree of complexity from the most simple to the most advanced. How is one to account for the fact that simple organisms endure from age to age without perceptible change? If we say that their complete adaptation to their environment is the cause of this inertia, then we have to say that there is no inevitable law of development: some other 'law' can suspend it.

However, even evolution as applied to the biological sphere, where it has always seemed valid and relevant, has long been in trouble concerning the mode and instrumentality of evolutionary change. Darwin himself held the idea of evolution to be unsatisfactory unless the mechanism of it could be explained. The Lamarckian doctrine of the inheritance of acquired characteristics was rather contemptuously rejected by biologists, though it is certain that Darwin accepted some, and Spencer, most of it. The Darwinian theory of natural selection rested upon a process of elimination of the least suitable types brought about by the struggle for existence working upon random variations. That left the variations unexplained. It was never very clear even in Darwin's day how even the struggle for existence could produce a change of *species*. Such a change was never actually observed. To demonstrate that it was possible, it would have been necessary to prove that not only were there somatic (bodily) differences between the survivors and the eliminated, but that there were *genetic* differences which led not simply to the somatic alteration of members of a species, but to a genetic transformation too.[1]

No satisfactory proof along these lines has ever been produced, and W. R. Thompson, F.R.S., in a very anti-Darwinian introduction to the 1956 Everyman Edition of *Origin of Species*, said this, 'We can, by selection, sort out from a natural population a number of pure lines or genotypes, each possessing with respect to a given character its special curve of variability, but we cannot change this curve by selection within the genotype. For example, in a certain pure line of housefly, those with the longest wings may conceivably have an advantage—though I cannot see how this could be demonstrated. But we cannot, by choosing and mating these long-winged flies, produce a progressive increase in the proportion of long-winged flies, or a progressive increase in wing length.'[2]

Since Darwin's day, of course, the simple doctrine of natural selection has been modified by Mendelian theories. It is now accepted by evolutionists, it seems, that the mutations of the genes responsible for somatic characteristics is the source of evolutionary change, and that these mutations are accidental. 'Mutation is the result of occasional inaccuracies in the various parts of the hereditary constitution, down to the ultimate units we call genes—failures to maintain some detail of their complicated physical and chemical structure; and these inaccuracies are then faithfully reproduced by the self-copying process, so that original mutation becomes a strain of mutant genes . . . mutation is the source of all heritable variation.'[3] But Julian Huxley is guessing. And his guess is: if evolution occurs, and if the hereditary machinery is as deliberately devised as anything could be to prevent a radical change in the species (and this is the truth which genetics reveals), then evolution must come about through a breakdown in the genetic machinery,

---

[1] *See* the discussion of the view of R. Pearl in Fothergill, *Historical Aspects of Organic Evolution*, pp. 321 et seq.

[2] Op. cit., Introduction, p. xii.

[3] *Evolution in Action*, J. Huxley, pp. 38-9.

not through the perfected functioning of it. Schrödinger, in *What is Life?*, argued that, since the gene is so resistant to change, only some act like bombardment by cosmic rays—a random process—could produce a mutation. W. R. Thompson has said in that introduction to *Origin of Species* to which I have already referred, that mutations are 'useless, detrimental, lethal'. Indeed, the whole genetic machinery seems to be designed to prevent the accidental mutation from operating to change the genotype. In nature, though not in the hothouse or stud farm, the mutants appear to have anti-survival characteristics. And in any case, chance particular mutants fail altogether to demonstra e how blended, or correlated, changes and adaptations in structure and functions take place in particular organisms. The chances that several useful mutations will occur simultaneously must be infinitely remote.

Whether natural selection in the old sense, or in the new sense of the struggle for existence working upon 'mendelizing mutations', can be held to explain how evolution took place, or whether indeed evolutionary theorists are not making exaggerated claims to knowledge, we may leave to the biologists to argue. The point simply has to be made that when so much about the actual process, method and motivations of evolution is, biologically speaking, obscure and speculative, it is highly improper to imagine that one can apply the theory of Natural Selection or of the Struggle for Existence, or some other evolutionary hypothesis, *to human history* with any great success, or that, though we can as yet barely explain occurrences in the field for which the evolutionary theory was invented, we can use it to illuminate the activities of a totally different order. In terms of scholarship, it is an improper proceeding. We can echo W. R. Thompson who said that he was 'not satisfied that Darwin proved his point or that his influence in scientific and public thinking has been beneficial'.

Of course, consciousness of the inadequacy of natural selection (whether or not added to Mendelism) to explain the evolutionary process has led to a crop of philosophies which have argued that some other principle governs the whole cosmic

31

process. One thinks of Bergson and his élan-vital, of Lloyd-Morgan and his law of Emergence, of Alexander's marriage of Time and Space, of Whitehead's philosophy of Organism, and of a host of others. But if we accept any one of these in place of Natural Selection as the governing principle operating inexorably throughout the cosmos, then we should expect it to demonstrate itself just as conclusively in the events of history as it does in biology, and if it does not, or does not postulate human exemption, then there must surely be something wrong either with our study of history or our biology, or with the principle we insist on applying indiscriminately to both of them.

In any case, even if we accept without cavil the evolutionary case, there is still a great deal of difference between driving a car and being a passenger in it, and if it is true that man has climbed into the driving seat of evolution—how has he got there, and what is he up to? If, on the other hand, 'man ended with the Pleistocene', if evolution in the old physical sense no longer controls man—ought we really to talk about it so glibly in the human connection? And if man has got free from evolution, then we have to ask, I think, how he has got free, and what new status he has acquired in relation to nature, and what new control has been given him over his own destiny. The point is, that if it is true that the final arbiter over all organisms is an evolutionary process, and if it is impossible that man should ever control it, for the simple reason that he cannot ever know what its 'orders' are, and even if he did, would not necessarily know how to countermand them, why then, historical inevitability is back again in the textbooks, whatever the professors say! If Marx and Spengler and Toynbee are rejected, but Darwin, Spencer, Haeckel, Keith and the Huxleys remain unchallenged still, there remains a law over history as unyielding as any which the scientists accept as governing nature: in fact, it is the same law, and 'history' is simply a branch of 'nature', or nature in another guise.

If therefore historical inevitability is to come under fire from historians, and human freedom is to be vindicated, then neither the historians nor the rest of us can be content to let things rest where they are. There is little point in exposing the absurdities and extravagances of a Hegel or a Marx, only to submit without protest to the sentence of animal stature which Darwin has pronounced upon mankind. It is for this reason that we have to decide what we mean by the sphere of history, and what we mean by the sphere of nature. We have to decide whether they overlap, and what it means if they do, and what it signifies after all if they are not identical.

CHAPTER 2

History and Nature

I

The word 'history' can mean three things. It can mean the aggregate of past events, or the study of that aggregate, or the making of the record. However, in the most general and popular sense, history is simply that which has happened. History therefore comes up to the present moment, and the course of it is still being woven mysteriously about us. But when we consider history as a pursuit or study we are better able to understand what history means as the aggregate of events. For though it is generally accepted that history is the aggregate of past events, no one is ever going to study that aggregate in its entirety. The student of history is not interested in the mere accumulation of factual detail, any more than the scientist is interested in the mere recording of facts. The counting of blades of grass in a field, if anyone should attempt it, would be as useless as it was arduous, though the total would certainly be information never previously obtained. The scientist would be indifferent to this information unless it pointed to a law or important relation, the fertility of the soil, for instance, or the comparative richness of strains of grasses, and even then he would seek to make his point with the minimum burden of facts. Indeed, the greatest problem faced by the research historian who chooses modern history as his field is the abundance of dead fact he has to winnow for the few grains of living truth.

History, if this be true, is the study of *significant* past events. Those events are usually public ones.

Is it valuable to make a distinction between public and private events in human history? If it can be properly maintained it will be found, I think, that such a distinction helps us to look at the differences between nature and history in a new light. Of course, public events rise out of private events, and the public and private events of the past are intertwined as lovingly as ivy-stems about the structure of history, but though we can never separate the private from the public event as sharply as we can separate the private from the public bath, we all recognize that there is a sense in which private events are not history, merely the soil of history. They do not become history unless they bear upon the general course of public events, and we must affirm this to be true even though certain public happenings begin as a distillation of many obscure or unknown private activities. It has been said, for instance, that the feelings of an angry mob will rise to an explosive pitch but will die away again unless there is something upon which they can expend their rage with a sense of justification. The necessary incident might as easily be provided by the strained nerves of some unknown but hysterical adolescent as by a trained and disciplined provocateur. A riot or even a revolution may be touched off upon the neurotic weakness of one despised youth who afterwards vanishes into obscurity and whose very name we never learn. Here, the behaviour of one individual appears to produce results out of all proportion to his importance, and the private becomes inextricably caught up with the public life.

Most private activities, however, are neutral in their bearing upon the course of history. It is of no public significance whether a man eats white or brown bread for breakfast, and the same is true of so many other things about a man's personal life—his choice of ties, his hobbies, the games he plays with his children, the flowers he chooses for his garden, these, with all their variations from man to man and town to town and country to country, are nevertheless so private that knowledge of them dies with the doer, and necessarily so, for information about

35

them is as publicly useless as would be a referendum which asked people whether they ate their eggs from the big end or the little one. And indeed, when information about private tastes and opinions is wanted, then very elaborate and costly machinery of enquiry—Gallup polls, street and class sampling, and mass observation—has to be set in motion to make public what remains usually so obdurately private.

It is true that the aggregates of these private, unknown and even personally forgotten choices and decisions form the current mode or fashion of living—they decide conventions, they create styles, they throw up a mysterious and ephemeral slang or jargon, they give birth to deep and unforeseeable social changes, and so there rises out of all of them that vast and mysterious thing which we call a culture and which we can recognize only at, so to speak, a comfortable historical distance. And it can so happen that nothing more brilliantly illuminates the public style, the heart of a culture, which we explore at a distance, than the revelation of a private and previously unknown life within it. What would we not give for the diaries of a serving maid of Helen of Troy, or the private papers of a secretary of Pontius Pilate, or the letters home of some unknown soldier during the days when Roman rule in Britain was crumbling? But this concession does not weaken my case. For it is we who, at a distance, would be giving private lives a public value. We should not dream of ploughing through thousands and thousands of similar revelations, were they vouchsafed to us, for repetition would diminish their importance, and dull our interest, and even defeat our aim, which must be in such cases to raise the particular to the height of universal significance.

Much of the inner significance of our private lives is lost for ever. We do not disclose it. It has no apparent effect on history. We are content that it should vanish with us. And when we are asked about history, we do not think of it in terms of our own ancestors, who may have led rich and colourful lives (though we may know nothing about them!), but as the history of our race or nation or civilization. We see what is private to us in a family sense as one thing, and what belongs to the public history as another. Even when we grow interested in a particular period of history, the Civil War or the Industrial Revolution, say, it hardly ever occurs to us that we had ancestors who went through those struggles and who valiantly took up arms, or were slily careerist, or unheroically timid or vacillating in the face of great events. We not only forget this, but we have no means of curing our ignorance about these ancestral activities if we should want to (unless we come of some great family which has kept its records). The familial past from which our being stems has vanished for most of us, and without any real resistance on our part to its oblivion. For what do ordinary people, workmen, clerks, teachers, priests, postmen and suchlike ever do to preserve what their parents have told them of their grandparents, let alone take up the task of filling out stories of their ancestors by research and investigation? They do nothing. The whole world does nothing. For it is true, and extraordinarily important too, that a family does not care about its own history in the way that its members care about their public history. It is content to let records die and ancestors be forgotten. The end-papers of family Bibles will sometimes contain records of family marriages, births, christenings and deaths, but they soon become dead book-keeping entries to which the living can no longer attach a familiar face or figure. Little or no living past comes down this way.

We must assert then that history is social for us, not private. For the public events we have histories, for the private lives, biographies, case-histories, or a silence as deep as that of interstellar space. It must be of the greatest importance that we decide to read our history socially and not privately, or by the family. If history really belongs to society, rather than to its biological and social unit, the family, then that is a clue to its meaning. But it is also a clue to the rôle of society in the life of man, for it suggests that society, considered as a whole, as that entity, be it tribe or city-state, or empire or nation, with which a man believes his being and his destiny to be bound up, society in that sense must have an importance transcending private and family life, even though it serves them and derives its authority from them. This I hope presently to explore in more detail.

II

The contrast between the value we attach to social and to family history leads us to a still more fruitful investigation, and that is into the difference between history and *nature*, or between the 'realm' of history and of nature. Perhaps this should involve us immediately in a search for definitions as to the nature of nature. But if one seeks to show the difference between history and nature this does not mean that one has to demonstrate that man is not a part of nature. The effort demanded of us is more subtle: it is to show that man lives in two dimensions, those of nature and of history, as the different valuations he places upon social and family history might after all lead us to suspect. There is no doubt that man is firmly planted in nature. We do not need to invoke evolutionary theory to prove it. Man has a physical body, many of the activities of which are autonomous and independent of his will, his flesh is animal flesh, his senses are improved or perfected versions of powers found in other mammals and even in organisms lower down the scale. Man is born of the flesh and can in nowise come into existence without the elaborate processes of physical reproduction which he shares with the dog and the hedgehog. All this is so obvious that we take it all for granted in day-to-day life. But if man were only that, if he lived only on the plane of the flesh, he would be one more animal among the vast hosts of animals, and there would be nothing to say, and no books to be written, for neither dogs, nor hedgehogs, nor whales nor elephants ask questions or make explanations. But man invents machines, writes symphonies, builds houses, studies the stars, founds great religions, goes mad, converses with God, and makes gothic gestures against his fleshly fate. Man cheats, lies, swindles, wrong-headedly sacrifices himself for bad causes, refuses to yield himself up to good ones, hoards as a miser, wastes his substance as a spendthrift, is guilty, anxious, self-tormenting, pretends to be what he isn't, despises what he is, is Hamlet and Othello, Oliver Twist and Don Quixote, Faust and Socrates. And all these human variations are achieved without any discernible alteration of the fleshly state of man, the animal structure. In fact, man is of the spirit as well as of the flesh, and his flesh is his natural inheritance and his history his spiritual one. In any event, it is because man cannot be successfully described in biological terms alone that there is a problem to be discussed. Or if we put it another way, man *can* be described in biological terms, but the description is puzzling, it leaves out too much; in fact, it is not recognizably about man.

Nature is sometimes described as the realm of the vital, but that is only another word for the living, and does not advance us very much. In fact, a definition of the natural will help us no more at this stage than a definition of the historical, for it is an exploration of these realms that we want, rather than dictionary definitions, and to this the whole book is bent. It is sufficient then to say that I mean by nature all that is living and is not human, but yet is the bed from which man sprang. With that nature man has great affinity and to it his body is still obedient. But still, man springs out of the bed. He cuts the umbilical cord. He is not content to stay within the realm of the natural. When a man satisfies his hunger or his thirst, or begets children, he is obeying a call of nature, and this is his first need, whatever other values may be added to the acts. But when he circumcises, or cicatrizes, with awesome ceremonial, a child of his tribes, he is not obeying any conceivable natural demand. His whole act, properly conceived, is an unnatural one. He is set upon the deformation or mutilation of nature, or the purging of the natural man at the call of some other, more imperious urge.

Nature, of course, has a 'natural history'. But this in no way helps us to reconcile nature and history. Human history is the study of significance among the aggregate of past human events. Natural history is the study of natural events and patterns, but by man, not by nature. So that natural history is almost a branch of human history. It is a concern of man, not of nature. Nature is indifferent to her own history. It can better be said that nature has no history. She acquires history only by entering the realm of the human, when all that occurs in nature borrows a new significance from that association.

'I conclude', wrote the late Professor R. G. Collingwood, 'that natural science as a form of thought exists and always has existed in a context of history, and depends on historical thought for its existence. From this I venture to infer that no one can understand natural science unless he understands history: and that no one can answer the question what nature is unless he knows what history is. This is a question which Alexander and Whitehead have not asked. And that is why I answer the question, "Where do we go from here?" by saying, "We go from the idea of nature to the idea of history." '[1]

Perhaps we can look again at the curious difference between our public and private lives. It is odd that our curiosities about our family life are negligible and those which are aroused by public history are almost inexhaustible. Obviously enough there is a parallel between the cycle of human generations, each in its turn slipping into oblivion, and the cycle of animal generations. This is one more example of the closeness of the human and animal situations. Each human generation lives its life in the light of the immediate sun, and then it is gone, and a new generation is in its place, dwelling in the houses it has vacated, usurping the powers it has abdicated, a generation as unheeding as those which went before. Many a man has stood at least once in his old school classroom obsessed with the feeling that the boys before him were usurpers, that it was they, not he, who were really the strangers in that place. And many a man has contemplated with grief the tide of the generations.

Richard Jefferies, standing at the Royal Exchange in the heart of London, where the millions pass, watched the fascinating traffic of people which he said 'fill the interstices between the carriages and blacken the surface, till the vans almost float on human beings. Now the streams slacken, and now they rush again, but never cease; dark waves are always rolling down the incline opposite, waves swell out from the side rivers, all

[1] *The Idea of Nature*, Oxford, 1945, the concluding paragraph.

London converges into this focus.' Here the human tide 'rushes and pushes, the atoms triturate and grind, and eagerly thrusting by, pursue their separate ends. Here it appears in its unconcealed personality, indifferent to all else but itself, absorbed and rapt in eager self, devoid and stripped of conventional gloss and politeness, yielding only to get its own way; driving, pushing, carried on in a stress of feverish force like a bullet, dynamic force apart from reason or will, like the force that lifts tides and sends the clouds onwards.' He asks, 'Where will be these millions of to-day in a hundred years? But, further than that, let us ask, Where then will be the sum and outcome of their labour? If they wither away like summer grass, will not at least a result be left which those of a hundred years hence may be the better for? No, not one jot! There will not be any sum or outcome or result of this ceaseless labour and movement; it vanishes in the moment that it is done, and in a hundred years nothing will be there, for nothing is there now.'[1]

Man, part of the human tide, subject to the cycle of the generations, is very close to the natural state, and shares the limitations it imposes. He lives a life which begins in feebleness and ends in death. A strict limit is set to it. He is no better off here than the lion and the rabbit. He has not even the advantage of the longest spell of life. The only difference between man and animals in respect of their submission to the natural cycle is that man understands the natural sentence under which he stands. The animal does not.

Of course, the difference is crucial. We have to search for a metaphor or an analogy which will enable us to illuminate this situation in order to throw light on the meaning of history. Suppose we consider a family travelling in a lighted railway carriage at night. In a cot a baby lies awake. The baby is too young to be aware of the motion of the travelling train: but it lives, as we have all lived, its own warm, comfortable life within the confines of the compartment. It stares at the light in the roof, at the framed pictures on the walls. It knows the parents which bend over it. The baby is like the animal. It is unaware

[1] *The Story of My Heart*. Edn. 1922, p. 95 et seq.

41

even that it is going on a journey, and its life is mostly sleep. But now think of a small boy in the carriage. He knows that he is on a journey. He knows that he is travelling in a train from one mysterious place to another. He has a strong sense of kinship with, a proud sense of belonging to, his family occupying the compartment and embarked on this remarkable enterprise. But he knows only the compartment in which he rides, and a few compartments on either side which he has timidly explored. He has not moved beyond his coach, and the rest of the train hardly exists for him. The small boy is like primitive man. Now consider the father of the family. He is aware of the whole train: he has walked through it. He has spoken to the guard. He knows the route and destination of the train and what passengers and freight it carries. He is like civilized man, a prisoner in his own restricted personal life but aware nevertheless that he is a part of the great procession of history moving through time.

The light from the carriage window is thrown on to the tracks in a narrow yellow band which moves rapidly forwards all the time across its continuum. That light, if we think of it as symbolizing the tiny world of the baby, can be compared with the span of awareness of the individual organism moving through time. In some creatures, which by the manner of their generation can have no awareness of parents or offspring, the band will be a mere slit of light, isolated from others of its kind. With man, and considering him for the present only as a part of nature, his personal band of light will overlap the bands of light not just of other individuals but of other generations. We may consider him for a moment as the small boy who knows the people in the other compartments on either side, and has taken them into his consciousness. Man's 'unhistorical' awareness extends backward for two or three generations, and forward perhaps for the same number. Yet compared with the feeble band of insect awareness, it is almost an arc light which 'unhistorical' man possesses.

Even so, this is hardly a matter for human pride. Beyond the span of three or four generations, which is all, empirically, personally, man can encompass, is the limbo of darkness into which, for most of us, the family past falls. And if this were the whole span of human knowledge—that which could be compressed within and digested by four generations—then the darkness over human affairs would be greater than that in which any savage we can name lives. In fact, man is rescued from the fate of the baby and the boy and brought to knowledge of the whole train and its route by what he calls history.

Between the paper-thin flicker of the insect's light, and the band of personal awareness which belongs to the individual, 'ahistorical' man, we must find a place for the situation of the mammal. The awareness of the rabbit seems to be limited to three contemporary generations, the parental, the subject's own, and that of its offspring. Yet even this needs qualification. The rabbit awareness is transitory and impermanent. It is quickly extinguished as generation succeeds generation in the fertile rabbit world. The infant rabbit knows its parents: the parent rabbit knows the infants. But once the infants have grown up, not even the doe gives any sign of 'knowing them'. Does she recognize them? All too quickly it would seem that knowledge dies, curiosity ceases. Only the immediate generation of the young is the concern of the doe. The evidence suggests that the mature rabbit is unaware that other adult rabbits of his burrow, with whom he will breed, are his offspring. Or if he is aware of it, he is not moved by it, it carries no consequences for him. Animal indifference to incest suggests ignorance of kinship once the dependence of immaturity is over. The adult male swan, the cob, conducts his male cygnets far away when they have grown up. If they seek to return with their parents to the place of their birth, they are driven off. If they manage nevertheless to come back they are met with the ferocity with which the wild swan treats any intruder, and harried to death. The family tie is deliberately broken. The animal admits no responsibility for his offspring after their maturity and often abandons them before. It suggests a total amnesia where the young which have grown up are concerned.

It does not appear that this situation is in any way changed where animals are gregarious. In a herd of deer the young stag is tolerated until he arrives at maturity and becomes a sexual rival. Then if he persists in remaining, he may be gored to death. The young does the old stag has sired remain as females sexually subservient to him. Packs of wolves or baboons are made up out of families, of course. But no family structure is maintained within the pack beyond that necessary for mating and the care of offspring. Apart from this, the internal structure of the pack is not affected by family relationships. The pack would not behave differently were all its members selected in a random way. It is even true that in collective animal societies like those of ants and bees, which would have most to gain by acquiring a history or even by extending the band of awareness across a few generations, there is just no sign that the collective oblivion is any less than that of the rabbit warren. After each winter hibernation the ant colony has to learn painfully once again the tracks, the pastures, the resources of its tiny empire.

Though, in his natural situation, as one of a particular generation indifferent to, forgetful of, vanished generations, man comes close to the animal situation, the differences are considerable nevertheless. Man's forgetfulness of the generations is of a different order from animal forgetfulness. The animal can forget the generation above it which gave birth to it, which is still living, which is even in Samuel Alexander's term, 'compresent' with it. It can forget too those generations which sprang from its loins of which perhaps a score are also compresent with it. The animal 'forgets' the living and compresent! Man 'forgets' the dead and sometimes the absent, but struggles to remember even them. So that we have to assert that the differences between the bands of awareness are far greater than were apparent at first sight. The animal escapes the narrow and egotistical concentration on its own immediate life only where there is a powerful organic link—to a mate, to a pack, to the procreation, feeding, and protection of offspring— but even this broadening of awareness does not appear to survive the occasion for it. It has, of course, often been said that an animal does not know that it was born and must die. It demonstrates no awareness of mortality, though it sometimes shows a willingness, even a need, to die. It manifests fear when faced with pain or danger or death. Though it may show panic, it seldom reveals grief in the presence of the death of others. There are exceptions to these rules, about which it may be possible to speak later, but perhaps all that I am saying is that the animal does not know that it is not immortal. It gives no awareness of the fatal and irreversible movement of time. Indeed, the limitations of its awareness are so great as to constitute a biological liability, which might result in the extinction of innumerable species, were it not for the fact that organisms possess a device aimed at overcoming the obvious danger of unawareness—I mean instinct. Instinct seems quite indefinable, but we can see what it does. It equips the individual organism with the power to respond to a situation *as if* it had personally experienced situations before just like it, *and learnt* how to deal with them. It is therefore in a way a racial memory, a means of overcoming the dangers inherent in a situation in which the organism cannot learn because it cannot remember. Without instinct the organism must meet situations which have occurred hundreds of times before as if nevertheless they were original and unique: that is, it would display time and time again the same total ignorance. It is almost as if *something* had elected to do the remembering for the organism, as a parent remembers for a child which is as yet incapable of understanding its own needs and making provision for them; as if the race or species across time were the organism, and the individuals of the species merely the body cells it produced. This is an analogy I dislike for many reasons, but it presses itself upon one unless one takes the step of speaking of the work of the spirit in the animal world. But when we think of the infant cuckoo born in this country and reared in the nest of a stranger and unacquainted with its own parents, making alone and uninstructed its migration flight to the winter habitat of its parents, then we are certainly faced with a mysterious racial memory, incarnate in each organism, or an equally mysterious transcendent instructing power.

45

Animal life seems often only one stage removed from the sleep of the vegetable kingdom. Much animal life seems spent in a kind of torpor. To gorge first, and then to sleep until hungry again is the natural inclination of most animals, except during the mating, or migration season, or some other disturbance of the normal round. And this predisposition to sleep and torpor (and therefore to the avoidance of struggle) is carried to striking lengths in those animals, reptiles, insects and plants which are actually able to suspend, or put in low gear, their life processes and annually hibernate in order to escape the most severe winter struggles for food and shelter which would otherwise engage them. The winter sleep of the tree, of the bear, and of the ant, are all one in this connection.[1]

Man, by comparison, even in his most simple and natural state (if there is such a thing) is very much aware of the conditions of his natural life: he knows that he was born, is alive, must marry and propagate, or else be without successors, must suffer pain and perhaps illness, must live on the whole precariously, and finally must die, and that for the whole of this natural situation he has no natural remedy. But this awareness, this waking situation, does not content him. He seeks continually to extend his awareness beyond the natural span of the generations to which he is committed by personal experience. He knows, and seeks to extend his knowledge of, what happened in other times and places with which neither personal nor family connection is possible. And so the analogy of the band of light fails us in the end, and must be abandoned. We might speak of the whole of nature as being a staircase and the bands of light as being illuminated steps of different sizes. In that case

---

[1] Hibernation: 'When a bat retires into hibernation all the internal activities of its body slow down to the lowest possible rate . . . the animal has stopped being "warm-blooded" and has approached as close to the dividing line between life and death as is possible for a mammal outside an experimental deep-freeze. . . . When a torpid bat is disturbed it is quite helpless—it slowly opens its mouth to squeak but no sound emerges, it gradually spreads its wings as it lies helpless in the hand, and gropes feebly in the air with its legs, and it may take many minutes to drag itself back from the brink of death.'

L. Harrison Matthews: 'The Bats Retire': *Observer*, 11th November 1956.

man has a step which is a broad plateau. But more, he stands
erect and aware upon it, torch in hand, and directs its beam
where he will—upon other steps, up the incline he is ascending,
upon himself, or waves it around in the dark night with which
he seems to be surrounded.

III

In the realm of nature life is cyclical, it returns upon itself, as
the Greeks imagined that history did. Just the most fascinating
aspect of natural life to man is the perennial repetition, the
dependable seasonal round, the blossom time and harvest
time, the swallows which return year after year to the eaves of
the same barn, and migrate again and again until their life's end
to their ancestral African haunts with the dependability of
transatlantic air liners. We are moved by the unrelenting
persistence of it all, by the endless cycle of the generations, by
the unchanging solitariness of the badger, the playfulness of the
kitten, the cunning of the fox and the fierceness of the tiger, so
reliable in their natures that they become permanent symbols
of human types. But the dependability of nature which is such
a source of joy, is also a source of grief, for civilized man longs
often to be able to act with the simplicity and directness of
nature, to act by instinct without either regret or foreboding, or
moral difficulties, and both the grief and the joy are the source
of a constant movement of man to achieve a harmony with
nature. Our imaginations are baffled by the soul or inner
being of an Assyrian shepherd, or a priest of Attis, or of Baal,
or a neophyte under Mithras or a rock-painter of Lascaux,
but we know that the snake, and the boar, and the stag and the
mosquito displayed to the earliest man the clear fixed natures
which they display to us.

We need not be troubled in this connection with evolution,
for we can easily misread what that evolutionary change means.
Indeed the sentimental romanticization of evolutionary change
is as we have seen the principal intellectual disability of our

47

age. Evolution, at least as interpreted by Sherrington rather than by Julian Huxley, tends to give us a picture of nature on the march which is entirely false. There is no evidence of a restlessness upon the part of living things (other than man) to be different from what they are. There is all the evidence to the contrary. No elephant or giraffe shows remorse or consternation at his natural state, and all the internal pressures of the organisms are as conservative as their external behaviour: they are designed to resist change, to restore the norm of the archetypal form, and to eliminate the freak or sport which might impair the stability of the species. The entire genetic mechanism of living things is intended to perpetuate every species just as it is, and to ensure that whatsoever individual variations from the norm may occur, every newly born creature starts afresh with the inherited qualities of the type, and is not conditioned or burdened by the acquired characteristics of the parents. What are we to say of an evolution in which certain ant forms appeared fifty to sixty million years ago and have persisted ever since without change, and in which others, held to have emerged thirty million years ago, are therefore described as recent innovations! If we remember this, and Julian Huxley's description of evolutionary blind alleys, and his suggestion that man alone continues the evolutionary process, we may be bold enough to say that nature displays anti-evolutionary powers and resistances. Nature drives towards the fixed type. Indeed to preserve certain forms unchanged through millions of years of changes in terrain, climate and environment is to assert that the very continents themselves are more plastic and malleable than certain natural forms.

The remorseless conservatism of the natural cycle, which we can picture as an endless longing for biological stability, comes not from the imperfections of living creatures, but from their perfections. And only against that natural stability, which I think we may be sure that the body of man shares, can we properly understand the intellectual disorder and spiritual restlessness of man.

In the realm of history, nothing is cyclical, nothing is sure, nothing is fixed, despite what the Greeks thought. We say that history repeats itself, but we only mean that similar situations recur. There will be tyrants again in human history who will be brought down by their own hubris, but there will not be Hitler again. There will be new revolutions, but not the Russian revolution, or the French revolution. There will be upheavals in thought and belief, but not the Reformation, or the decades of Darwin and Huxley, or the birth of Christ, again. It would seem that every historical event is unique, in the same sense that every man is unique, non-recurrent.

If what I have said about man is true, if, that is to say, in his family and his personal life man belongs in a certain sense to the natural cycle, and if on the other hand he belongs in another sphere of himself to the historical, to the uncyclical movement, to the linear voyage of the spirit, we are faced with a great enigma. *How* has this come to pass? How has this perfectly good animal escaped the animal cycle? Or to put it another way, why could not man have stopped within the natural cycle? *Could* he have done? He had as much, but no more reason than the ant or the bee for establishing a 'history'. Considered as many evolutionists would like to consider him, man could have lived a purely natural cyclical life, as the gibbon and chimpanzee for long ages have continued to do, and it would seem must continue to do down to the end of time. Why did they stay where they are, and man move out of it?

There have been movements of thought in our time—would to God they had only been movements of *thought*—which longed for a restoration of a 'natural' man, and an end to the civilized one. But whether or not early man could have lived within the natural cycle, he certainly did not. He came out of it, and it is impossible for man, having come out of it, ever to go back into it. To do so he would have to forget his history, and man does not forget his history by having theories like those of Jean-Jacques Rousseau or D. H. Lawrence about how it went wrong. Far from forgetting his history, man resists just that disaster, in whatever state of society we find him. He insists upon living the historical life, and almost everything he does—even when

D   49

supposedly aimed in a contrary direction—heightens his historical life, and emphasizes the unique, the irreplaceable in the human situation. The impulse is so strong among primitive peoples that in default of a genuine historical record to which they can grapple themselves, they are prepared to invent one.

CHAPTER 3

A Flowering of Apes

I

At some point in time man broke free from the natural cycle. Whether he did so as man, or whether he did so in order to become man is perhaps insoluble. However, the problem need not concern us at this stage. It is more important to establish if we can the fundamental conditions of the first human state. Yet to undertake this task involves us in insuperable difficulties, for we ought to look at the most primitive of human societies: but primitive societies which are also new, pristine, do not exist in our world. The most primitive of contemporary societies must have behind it a history of thousands of years. Australian aborigines, for example, perhaps the most primitive of contemporary men, use languages in ritual and ceremony from which all meaning has long vanished even for them, languages which have come down from a completely mysterious past. And this, indeed, is a commonly reported feature of savage religious life. It caused Alain Gheerbrant to say, when recording the religious rites of the primitive Piorias, 'Apparently the Indians had their own "Latin" for religious purposes.'[1]

The primitive societies the anthropologists study must be old and sophisticated in comparison with the first societies of emergent humanity. They may even be degenerate. We cannot possibly know. Certainly it is wrong to assume that they are change-

[1] *Impossible Adventure*, London 1955, p. 133.

less. The best we can do is to look at primitive societies as we find them, bearing in mind their certain antiquity, and try to discover what forces move them, and to what end. And here is our hope, for sometimes we find that they become transparent, and we can look through them, as down the wrong end of the telescope, and see, or imagine that we see, thrillingly at the bottom, in miniature but nevertheless sharply defined, the unmistakable lineaments of our most primitive human ancestors.

Yet what we make of such a vision depends on our approach to the primitive, about which popular misconceptions and romanticisms are legion. Either primitive society is thought to be all demons and cruelties and ignorance, or else it is thought to be all life and dancing spontaneity and naturalness, or else, somehow, both light and dark at once and therefore superior in natural and emotional endowments to the civilized world. The notion of the primitive man as the paradisal man which we can derive from Jean-Jacques Rousseau or Tacitus or from D. H. Lawrence or Malinowski has taken so many hard knocks in our day that we can safely disregard it, recognizing it for what it is, not so much a description of the primitive as a criticism of contemporary society, as indeed the source of one of the ideologies of the modern world. But the other notion of the primitive, as the dark and oppressive society, is equally misleading and has also to be cleared away. Dr. Karl Popper, in his searching political study, *The Open Society and its Enemies*,[1] based his attacks on Fascism and Communism on the contrast between what he chose to call 'tribal' societies and open societies. His 'open' societies are democratic, rational and experimental while the tribal society of his definition is backward-looking, obedient to the elders, hostile to change.

'When I speak of the rigidity of tribalism,' Dr. Popper wrote, 'I do not mean that no changes can occur in the tribal ways of life. I mean rather that the comparatively infrequent changes have the character of religious conversions or revulsions, or of the introduction of new magical taboos. They are not based upon a rational attempt to improve social conditions. Apart

[1] London, 1945.

from such changes—which are rare—taboos rigidly regulate and dominate all aspects of life. They do not leave many loopholes. There are few problems in this form of life, and nothing really equivalent to moral problems.'[1]

In fact, Popper holds, freedom in the civilized sense threatens the whole established pattern of tribal life, without the support of which the tribesmen believe that they will perish.

Professor Popper illustrated his thesis from classical Greece where he found evidence of the struggle between the closed tribal form of society and the open, dynamic, democratic society of Periclean Athens. Although the contrast Popper made is important, his use of the term 'tribal' is suspect. He speaks of 'Platonic totalitarianism and tribalism', of 'Hegel and the New Tribalism', or 'propaganda for a return to tribalism' which reveals that he uses 'tribal' in a pejorative sense for something he dislikes politically. Indeed, we see why he does so, for his theme grew out of the tragedies of our time and his work attempts to show that our Western 'civilization has not yet fully recovered from the shock of its birth—the transition from the tribal or "closed society", with its submission to magical forces, to the "open society" which sets free the critical powers of man. It attempts to show that the shock of this transition is one of the factors that have made possible the rise of those reactionary movements which have tried, and still try, to overthrow civilization and to return to tribalism. And it suggests that *what we call nowadays totalitarianism belongs to a tradition which is just as old or just as young as our civilization itself.*'[2]

Yet this is very arbitrary. The effort to equate 'tribal' with 'totalitarian' is simply to read into primitive societies the tensions and despairs of our own. There is no warrant for it. If it is successful it can only produce another political myth of the kind Professor Popper castigates when he meets it in Marx and Hegel. It is impossible for instance to see how either the Manus society of New Guinea, or the Samoan society, both felicitously described by Margaret Mead, and both satisfactorily primitive,

[1] *The Open Society and its Enemies*, Vol. I, p. 172.
[2] Ibid., p. 1 (Italics mine).

can be described in totalitarian terms: nor for that matter can the label be applied to the societies of the Eskimos, the Bushmen, or the Australian aborigines. Of course, primitive society can be bloody, cruel, persecuting, and dominated by magic: it can also be free, easy-going, unable or unwilling to compel adherence to its mores and traditions except by ostracism and outlawry, and sometimes not even by these. Even in cases of breaches of taboos it does not follow that the primitive society takes any action: it often believes the actions follow from outraged spirits, and therefore it needs to do nothing itself, for the revenge that will surely follow is out of its hands. Some societies may, however, be moved to cruel action: there is no certain guide, for the differences between primitive societies are so great that the anthropologist is compelled to speak of them in terms of separate cultures. What is certainly true is that no parallel of any importance can be drawn with totalitarian societies, not even with those which believe that they are retracing their steps to the tribe. For such totalitarian societies when they are bloody, cruel and persecuting are so, not because they live in a world saturated with spirit forms to be magically appeased, but for deep-seated and carefully thought out and thoroughly evil reasons. The tribal society can do monstrous things without becoming itself monstrous. The totalitarian society deliberately creates a monstrous instrument of power in order at once to perform and hide its monstrous deeds. It is deeply aware of what it is doing, and the tribal unity it is supposed to be hankering for is a sophisticated modern doctrine. It is a real perversion of history to imagine that when a civilized society degenerates it becomes 'primitive'.

It is a mistake to assume that the choice which is open to *contemporary* primitive societies—either to remain tribal or to adopt civilized ways—was always open to the primitive. That is to be doubted. The primitive society had a special task to perform in what Margaret Mead has described as the countless experiments man has made with the possibilities of the human spirit. It had to secure the human situation against the pressures and catastrophes of *nature*: it had to conquer the territory which civilizations were later to occupy and exploit. It pioneered the human order, and often with brilliant success. It was this unique rôle in territory where there were no tracks, no guides, no precedents, which makes the story of such primitive societies as we are able to examine such a fascinating one, and that alone should make us wary of judging them in the light of the twentieth-century political adventures and ideological struggles of a civilization old and torn enough to be threatened with decay.[1]

There is a very great danger in Professor Popper's line of analysis of the primitive: all too easily we can make the assumption that the civilized society is the only *really* human society, which is precisely what Bertrand Russell did in *Human Society in Ethics and Politics* when he said that, 'It is only about six thousand years since man discovered his capacity for distinctively human activities. These began, we may say, with the invention of writing and the organisation of government.' What endless human contrivance such a statement dismisses! As though tools, houses, swords, armour, agriculture, totemism, circumcision, sacrifice, dress, dance, gods—the list is endless—which are older than six thousand years are simply forms or extensions of animal powers and activities. If the argument, so flattering to us, of the non-humanity of early man is laboured, only the urbane and polished and highly civilized begins to bear for us a recognizably *human* face. To emphasize our exalted state it becomes important to blacken the uncivilized man. We conceive of our forebears as stunted by the state of nature, as living in 'continual fear, and danger of violent death; and the life of man, solitary, poor, nasty, brutish, and short', as Thomas Hobbes put it in an immortal sentence.

We rather owe this conceited way of looking at primitive man to Charles Darwin, who wrote, 'The astonishment which I felt on first seeing a party of Fuegians on a wild and broken shore will never be forgotten by me, for the reflection at once

---

[1] I am not concerned to play down this struggle, simply to say that we must be careful over our choice of intellectual weapons, and I do not think that Professor Karl Popper is. I have discussed the crisis of our century in two works, *The Annihilation of Man* (London, 1944, New York, 1945) and *The Age of Terror* (London, 1950, Boston, 1951).

rushed into my mind—such were our ancestors. These men were absolutely naked and bedaubed with paint, their long hair was tangled, their mouths frothed with excitement, and their expression was wild, startled, and distrustful. They possessed hardly any arts, and like wild animals lived on what they could catch; they had no government, and were merciless to everyone not of their own small tribe. He who has seen a savage in his native land will not feel much shame, if forced to acknowledge that the blood of some more humble creature flows in his veins.'[1]

I do not really need to defend the essential humanity of the Fuegians. Their primitive savagery was at least in part to be attributed to the desperate effort to survive in a bleak and cruel land where even a party of Manchester cotton brokers would hardly have done better. Yet it certainly illuminates the point of view I am criticizing that Darwin went on in that same passage to speak of savage man as inferior in morals and in heroism to monkeys and baboons, and if such an argument were seriously pressed, it would mean indeed that primitive man, savage man, would have to be demoted to a rank below the apes and the new and old world monkeys.

It is all the more necessary then to remind ourselves that the professional anthropologist rejects this tendentious kind of approach most earnestly. Speaking of his discipline, Professor Carleton Coon of Harvard wrote: 'One rule which this discipline has taught us is to avoid value comparisons between cultures. As members of the anthropological profession, we in America believe both in the rights of individuals to live at peace with each other within societies, and in the rights of separate societies and cultures to coexist in the world.'[2]

He goes on to say that he accepts the declaration of the Executive Board of the American Anthropological Association, sent to the Human Rights Commission of the United Nations, which firmly asserts that there is no technique for 'qualitatively evaluating cultures'. True, Professor Coon then proceeds in his valuable study to try to measure cultural levels by what he

---

[1] *The Descent of Man*, London, 1922, p. 946.
[2] *A Reader in General Anthropology* by C. S. Coon, London, 1950, p. vii.

describes as a *quantitative* method, which seems a way of smuggling in a value judgment by the back-door, but his assertion of the need for an approach to the primitive free from pre-judgments about it remains most significant. For the first and most important thing is to try to see it in its own light. It seems to me that it is in Professor Arnold Toynbee's *Study of History* that we find the most understanding estimate of the rôle of the primitive man in human history:

'Primitive societies, as we know them by direct observation, may be likened to people lying torpid upon a ledge on a mountainside, with a precipice below and a precipice above; civilizations may be likened to companions of these sleepers who have just risen to their feet and have started to climb up the face of the cliff above; while we, for our part, may liken ourselves to observers whose field of vision is limited to the ledge and the foot of the upper precipice and who have come upon the scene at the moment when the different members of the party happen to be in these respective postures and positions. At first sight we may be inclined to draw an absolute distinction between the two groups, acclaiming the climbers as athletes and dismissing the recumbent figures as paralytics; but on second thoughts we shall find it more prudent to suspend judgment.'[1]

As he explains, the sleeping figures could not have been born upon the ledge, and no other muscles but their own could have hoisted them up. And before we hasten to condemn them and to praise the others who are still climbing, it will be best to wait until we see what happens to the climbers. For though the climbers are those who have left primitive society, and this is at least a tribute to their courage, we cannot say that they will arrive at the next resting place. 'And we can observe that, for every single one now strenuously climbing, twice that number (our extinct civilizations) have fallen back on to the ledge, defeated.'

And Toynbee seeks to expose in Genesis myths, and redemption myths of the struggle between divine antagonists for the

[1] Abridgement of Vols. I-VI, by D. C. Somervell, London, 1946, pp. 49-50.

soul of man, the decision of man to renounce the old gods, and to seek knowledge and power for himself, and so to break from the fixed primitive order, from his first state of integration, and to accept the perils and uncertainties of the new and unexplored for the sake of the prizes it may offer. And so, Toynbee reasons, 'The picture of Adam and Eve in the Garden of Eden is a reminiscence of the Yin-state to which primitive man attained in the food-gathering phase of economy, after he had established his ascendancy over the rest of the flora and fauna of the Earth. The Fall, in response to the temptation to eat of the Tree of knowledge of Good and Evil, symbolizes the acceptance of a challenge to abandon this achieved integration and to venture upon a fresh differentiation out of which a fresh integration may —or may not—arise. The expulsion from the Garden into an unfriendly world in which the Woman must bring forth children in sorrow and the Man must eat bread in the sweat of his face, is the ordeal which the acceptance of the Serpent's challenge has entailed. The sexual intercourse between Adam and Eve, which follows, is an act of social creation. It bears fruit in the birth of two sons who impersonate nascent civilizations: Abel the keeper of the sheep and Cain the tiller of the ground.'[1]

A stimulating analysis, of the kind which Toynbee does to perfection! But is it true? Could not the myth be read in other ways? What is there secure or idyllic in the food-gathering stage of humanity? Is not this the least rewarding and most dangerous of all stages of human life? Must it not produce its barren days of search, the homelessness of perpetual wanderers, the certain hungers of winter, and thrust the searching man, woman and child into every kind of danger from enemies both large and small? Alain Gheerbrant describes the life of the primitive Guaharibos in terms that make painful reading. They had only one tool, a broken pebble spliced to a stick, and so their huts were primitive and rickety, every bough and branch having to be torn almost by hand to fit a shelter. They were frightened and lost and dangerous as hungry dogs might be. Here was perhaps a man even more primitive than the Australian abor-

[1] Ibid., pp. 65-6.

igine, and in comparison with such an existence, even deliberately organized hunting of large game is to be preferred, and as against both such means of livelihood, the keeping of sheep or the tilling of soil promise social security and a higher standard of living. Indeed, the food-gatherers may have hungered for such security just as the nomadic children of Israel coveted the land flowing with milk and honey. After their migration, Palestine was no challenge to destiny but a safe harbour reached after much suffering.

And is the sexual intercourse which follows the fall in Genesis myths symbolic of the birth of two civilizations—or is it more nearly what it says, the discovery of sexual intercourse, not in the sense of its first occurrence, of course, but of the first psychological awareness of it, and therefore its association with shame and fear such as every man comes to in his individual life as he grows out of infancy? The Genesis myths, in their own right (that is by their own claim), deal with the creation of the world and the creation of man. For the scribes of the Jewish civilization who in the days of Persian dominance of their land brought all the oral traditions into one consistent story, the task could hardly have been one of giving an account of the rise of the civilization itself. For about that they knew. The exodus, the wanderings in the desert, and the conquest of the Promised land —this was the history or the legend which accounted for that. The Genesis story had a far harder task—that of giving an account of the agonies of spirit by which man first became man. And perhaps in this the symbolism of Genesis is authoritative.

No, it was the decision to become man which was so full of peril, not the decision to leave a primitive society for a more settled and civilized one. It seems to me therefore that most of Toynbee's mythical instances could more properly belong to the first emergence of man, rather than to the second and long-delayed step of man into civilization. Indeed, I find that Toynbee quotes two modern historians in support of his argument, and their points of view perhaps more properly support mine.

'Ages ago a band of naked, houseless, fireless savages started from their warm home in the torrid zone, and pushed steadily northward from the beginning of spring to the end of summer. They never guessed that they had left the land of constant warmth until in September they began to feel an uncomfortable chill at night. Day by day it grew worse. Not knowing its cause they travelled this way or that to escape. Some went southward, but only a handful returned to their former home. There they resumed the old life, and their descendants are untutored savages to this day. Of those who wandered in other directions, all perished except one small band. Finding that they could not escape the nipping air, the members of this band used the loftiest of human faculties, the power of conscious invention. Some tried to find shelter by digging in the ground, some gathered branches and leaves to make huts and warm beds, and some wrapped themselves in the skins of the beasts they had slain. Soon these savages had taken some of the greatest steps towards civilization. The naked were clothed; the houseless sheltered; the improvident learnt to dry meat and store it with nuts for the winter, and at last the art of preparing fire was discovered as a means of keeping warm. Thus they subsisted where at first they thought that they were doomed. And in the process of adjusting themselves to a hard environment they advanced by enormous strides, leaving the tropical part of mankind far in the rear.'[1]

The second quotation, from J. L. Myres' *Who were the Greeks?*, links this monumental step forward in human history directly with the Ice Ages:

'It is . . . a paradox of advancement that, if necessity be the mother of invention, the other parent is obstinacy, the determination that you will go on living under adverse conditions rather than cut your losses and go where life is easier. It was no accident, that is, that civilization, as we know it, began in that ebb and flow of climate, flora and fauna, which characterizes the four-fold "Ice Age". Those primates who just "got out" as arboreal conditions wilted retained their primacy among the servants of natural law, but they forewent the conquest of

[1] *Civilisation and Climate* by Ellsworth Huntington, New Haven, 1915, pp. 287-8.

nature. Those others won through, and became men, who stood their ground when there were no more trees to sit in, who "made do" with meat when fruit did not ripen, who made fires and clothes rather than follow the sunshine; who fortified their lairs and trained their young, and vindicated the reasonableness of a world that seemed so reasonless.'[1]

Those passages seem to me quite to contradict Toynbee's main theme. Was it Homo Sapiens who came in, and the primate who went out, when certain ape-like creatures stood their ground before the Ice Ages? Was that the moment of transformation which gave birth simultaneously to man *and* to civilization? Not certainly by the scale of Toynbee, who speaks of the 300,000 years of primitive societies before the emergence of the first, almost contemporary civilization, which he puts at about 6,000 years ago. Or was it, as Ellsworth Huntington would suggest in his parable, as he calls it, simply a savage, one already a man by whatever standards we apply, who was tested, and faced the test, who gave birth to those technical inventions which saved him from extinction, and who therefore took 'some of the greatest steps towards civilization', while his more timid contemporaries retreated to Africa and contracted out of the struggle for ever? In order to see what truth there is in these vivid pictures it is necessary to look at what the authorities say about the origins of true man.

II

In his own arbitrary way the geologist breaks the history of the earth into eras. Not very consistently, they are named the Archaean, the Palaeozoic, the Mesozoic, the Tertiary and the Quaternary—which is our own. Even in the rocks of the Archaean era some geologists claim to discover traces of obscure life, at least in the late Pre-Cambrian rocks, which would suggest that life originated on the planet more than 2,000 million years ago. By the end of the Palaeozoic, that is roughly 195

[1] Op. cit., pp. 277-8.

million years ago, the invertebrates, fishes, amphibia and reptiles were firmly established. The Mesozoic era saw the emergence of birds, and the Tertiary the evolution of the mammal.
The story of man's origins does not really commence until the
Miocene period which began 35 million years ago. 'The
Lower Miocene seems to have been a period during which apes
produced new genera and species at a tremendous rate; this
sudden exuberance is noticed over and over again in the evolution of many forms of life and has been called "explosive
evolution".'[1] Yet only at the end of the Pliocene period—perhaps 34 million years later—did men-like creatures, it is asserted,
first see the light. It is in the deposits of the Pleistocene and
Holocene geological systems that we find the fossilized remains
of Homo Sapiens, and evidence of his activities and his tools in
cave earths and the remains of primitive hearths and among
the washings of river terrace gravels, and other such places.
Man the tool-maker certainly existed at the beginning of the
Pleistocene, that is more than 500,000 years ago. And if we
look at time with some cosmic piety, and treat it less cavalierly
than the average scientist, if that is to say we really seek to conceive of that span of time in human terms, in terms of human
generations, or measured against the scale of the life of nations
or of civilizations, then on that scale we must be overwhelmed
by human antiquity in the same way that we are awed when we
stare into the blackness of a well which seems to have no
bottom.

Man has been described, inimitably, as 'a unique bipedal
mammal, equipped with grasping hands that are capable of
fine work, with fine-focusing stereoscopic eyes, with a brain
unique for its large size, and with vocal organs capable of pro-
ducing the sounds needed in speech'.[2] This bipedal mammal
belongs to the order of primates (most of which are quadra-
pedal, however), which includes such creatures as anthropoid
apes and monkeys, and lemurs, tree-shrews and tarsiers, a
group of versatile creatures whose remarkable differences arise

[1] *Prehistory of East Africa*, Sonia Cole, London, 1954, p. 66.
[2] *The History of Man*, Carleton S. Coon, London, 1955, p. 4.

from successful evolutionary adaptation to different habitats and ways of life. All the primates are said to have sprung from some common primitive ancestor in the chalk period perhaps 100 million years ago.

It is interesting to see how man's place in the order of primates is arrived at by the process of classification based on comparative anatomy, for this will help us to see the difficulties the professors face in deciding man's origin. The Primatial Order is divided into two sub-orders, the Anthropoidea, and the Prosimii. The Anthropoid order includes the new and old world monkeys, and the family or super-family, of Hominoidea, which includes Man and the anthropoid apes. Of course, the grouping of Man with the Apes is meant to indicate the close structural resemblance between them. And if one is to accept the general evolutionary argument that animals are to be classified according to the greater degree of complexity, man stands upon a higher scale than the ape. Is he then descended from the ape? 'It has been vigorously denied that Man has ever been derived from an anthropoid ape, on the grounds that an "anthropoid ape" is an arboreal animal showing certain divergent specializations of an adaptive nature, such as are to be found in modern apes, and which would presumably be absent in any form ancestral to Man. But such a definition of "anthropoid ape" is far too narrow, for it only applies to certain end-products of evolution represented by the *existing* apes. The category of "anthropoid apes" must be taken to indicate not only these end-products but also all those intermediate types which have come into existence since the progenitors of the group first became segregated in their evolutionary history from the progenitors of other groups of Primates.'[1] Sir Wilfred Le Gros Clark does not therefore rule out the possibility that one of these early unspecialized anthropoid apes may have been the true ancestor of man. And there is a candidate for this post, as we shall see. But the process of classification hesitates, and subdivides the Hominoidea into Hominidae and Pongidae, into those which walk on two feet and those which walk on four.

[1] *History of the Primates*, Sir W. E. Le Gros Clark, London, 1956, p. 48.

And this actually begs the question, for instead of deriving the Hominidae from the Pongidae, it postulates in fact and of necessity a common ancestor for them both, though it cannot name it with any certainty. And so the ancestral tree of man, as usually drawn by the comparative anatomists and the palaeontologists, shows the line of man and the line of the anthropoid apes uniting in the later Tertiary, that is well over a million years ago. It then shows that joint line uniting with the old world monkeys (Cercopithecoidea) in the early Tertiary, and so it carries the story of man's origin back to an order springing from the early Primates in the chalk period.

What is the common ancestor of Man and the Anthropoid apes? Scholarship must hesitate because in some things 'man himself is actually more primitive and generalized than the modern anthropoid apes'[1] and if those things alone counted it would be more useful to derive the ape from a kind of human stock than man from a kind of ape stock. This idea is less fantastic than it seems, for to find a common ancestor to them both presupposes that the ancestor will show more specifically human characteristics than the modern ape. That is almost the first qualification, since the arboreal specializations of the ape might have caused him to branch away from a stock nearer the human.

The most likely candidate for the ancestor of man and the anthropoid apes is the Proconsul ape, a creature from the Miocene period, perhaps 30 million years ago, the tiny, fragile, baby-like skull of which was discovered by Dr. Leakey on Rusinga Island in 1948. The virtues of the Lilliputian Proconsul are that it lacks specialization of the skull and limbs. It is without a great ape-like ridge across the brow, it is without a simian shelf; and the dental arch and structure, and articulation of the jaws, are more human than those of the apes. The limb bones are not yet those of a brachiating ape or those of bipedal man: they could have given rise to either. Even the foot of the Proconsul was more adapted to rapid running than to tree-swinging.

[1] Ibid., p. 34.

The only serious challenge to the candidature of Proconsul has come recently from Dr. Johannes Hurzeler of Basel Natural History Museum. He has looked again at the fossil fragments discovered in the Miocene of Tuscany of the Orepithecus, a large fossil monkey of the Miocene: this creature exhibits characteristics which appear to foreshadow the anthropoid apes. But Dr. Hurzeler believes that here is a direct ancestor of man and argues from this that man came into existence with other primates at the end of the Mesozoic period or the beginning of the Tertiary, perhaps therefore 100 million years ago.

A more likely candidate for the ancestor of man *alone* is to be found among the Australopithecines—fossil apes of the Miocene —'just the sort of ancestor one would expect for man, at a stage when the Hominidae branched off from the Hominoidea,' Mrs. Sonia Cole remarks.[1] The specimens of skulls and bones of this ape discovered in cave deposits in Bechuanaland show that it combined both simian and human features. Its skull is lofty and rounded compared with that of a gorilla. The eyebrow ridges are far less prominent, and from the skeletal evidence of the way in which the skull of this ape was articulated at the top of the spinal column it is possible to argue that the Australopithecine was much more erect and human in gait than any modern ape. The teeth, too, are more human. But what was this creature? Despite the skull shape, the brain was no greater in size than that of a modern large ape, which is to say that it was no more than half the human size. The anthropologists assure us that the Australopithecine was not a man. No tools, no implements, no evidence of the use of fire have been discovered with the fossil remains. There is nothing to tell us that the creature could speak. Only one curious factor points towards higher intelligence than that granted to the primates contemporary with it, and that is that the skulls of baboons have been found on Australopithecine sites which have fractures suggesting that they were killed by deliberate blows, therefore that Australopithecines might have been hunters of other primates, and in that sense superior to them. This creature might very sensibly

[1] *The Prehistory of East Africa*, p. 70.

be cast for the ancestor of man, but it is doubtful if it could be cast for the ancestor of modern apes too. The skull of the Australopithecine so much foreshadows the human, that to derive the modern ape from it presupposes an evolutionary degeneration on the part of the ape, a flattening of the skull, a shrinkage of brain power, the loss of ability to walk upright, a refusal of the nearly human in favour of something more primitive and isolated, for the apes are evolutionary failures compared with man.

Yet before it can be argued seriously that the Australopithecines were the ancestors of Homo Sapiens, it is necessary to show at least that they are older than the Pithecanthropus Robustus, the Java man, who flourished half a million years ago. For it is quite possible that the Australopithecines were yet another family of primates contemporaneous either with the first man, or the ancestors of true men, which subsequently died out. The remains of the Australopithecines come from the Lower Pleistocene beds, and it is in these beds too, if at a higher level, that we find also the remains of Pithecanthropus Robustus and of the Heidelberg man, a neanderthal type, and if the jaw fragment discovered in Kana, on the shores of the Kavirondo Gulf in Kenya in 1932, has been correctly assessed as to geological dating and anatomical characteristics—and a Cambridge conference was held to decide just these things— then the lower Pleistocene yields also our first evidence of Homo Sapiens. The experts have already decided that Homo Sapiens must be placed (in time of origin) before Homo Neanderthalensis, and this can only mean that the finer, more developed man appeared before the more squat, thick-skulled apelike creature which is the caricaturist's prototype.

The Pithecanthropus—the Java man and the Pekin man— show many apelike features: a receding forehead, a sharply pointed skull at the back to which must have been attached powerful neck muscles, a broad flat nose, powerful jaws with an apelike muzzle—and no chin in the human sense. The teeth, however, conform to a human rather than an ape structure. Such fossil limbs as have been found indicate that the Pithecanthropus was much closer to man in his modelling and proportions than to an ape. Yet this dwarfish, beetle-browed creature of low intelligence manufactured tools from such a difficult material as quartz, and he had learnt the use of fire, and cooked his meat and roasted his meat bones. It has been suggested that he practised cannibalism and may have been a head-hunter after the fashion of the tribes in the interior of Borneo and New Guinea.

When we move our investigation into the Middle Pleistocene then we are already faced with unmistakable evidence of the antiquity of true Homo Sapiens. In a gravel pit at Swanscombe in Kent in 1935 and 1936 a Mr. A. T. Marston discovered bones from a human skull in Middle Pleistocene layer which also yielded fossil remains of extinct animals. Flint implements were found with the bones. All the evidence points to the existence here of true man in an early phase of palaeolithic culture. In fact, as the evidence in general accumulates the tendency is to push back the date of the origin of man. However, there is as yet no conclusive evidence which would enable us to construct that genealogical tree so much longed for by evolutionary propagandists showing the emergence of Homo Sapiens through a graded series of Hominoidea. The sensible conclusion to which Professor Carleton Coon comes is this: 'Until we discover otherwise it is safer to assume that all the ape-men, half-brained men, full-brained men with muzzles and members of the species Homo Sapiens which have been discovered so far, and others awaiting discovery, existed at the beginning of the Pleistocene, than to build up an evolutionary scheme within Pleistocene times on the basis of the relative dates of the few fossils that have yet appeared.'[1] And all this rather adds interest to the argument of Dr. Johannes Hurzeler that the great flowering of the primates took place at the end of the Mesozoic—at which time Homo Sapiens himself appeared, who is therefore older as a species than the Proconsul, which then becomes purely an ancestor of the apes. As the evidence accumulates, the gaps in the story of early man will be filled in, but it is of course

---

[1] *History of Man*, p. 25.

the very accumulation of evidence which is pushing the calculation of man's origin farther and farther back. Sonia Cole's argument about a flowering of ape forms in the Lower Miocene—that is very nearly 35 million years ago—must not be forgotten: it is very conceivable that this period saw the birth of someone we should recognize as Homo Sapiens.

It is important to understand the handicaps which accompanied the translation of our ancestor to manhood. It would seem that before the ancestral primate gave rise to the ancestral homo, several simultaneous changes in bodily structure had to take place. The ancestral primate had to rise from his four paws and walk erect and had to use his forepaws for handling objects. But it was not simply a question of new muscular adaptations. There had to be changes in the skeleton. The foramen magnum, the hole in the base of the skull through which the spinal column passes, was shifted to allow the head to be held erect. There were corresponding modifications of the spinal column and the pelvis in shape and alignment to take the new shifts of weight and the new tensions of muscles to permit locomotion by means of the hind limbs. The direction of sight had to be shifted so that it lay at right angles to the brain and the spine, instead of in line with them. A foot, perhaps previously adapted to tree-swinging, is not of much use for rapid running movements. There was therefore a modification of the tarsal pattern to produce a walking and running rather than a grasping or climbing foot. Erect posture and ground walking free the hands for grasping and handling objects. An enormous advance! But handling, grasping, manipulating objects with the hand involve a delicate co-ordination of sight and touch as well as the acquisition of new muscular skills: and without additional brain space for the cerebral end of this process the new skills could not have come into existence. In fact, man has double the brain capacity of the ape.

I cannot imagine how many simultaneous, transmissible mutations would be necessary to bring into existence this complicated bodily reorganization which would permit ancestral man, crude and clumsy as he was, to rise above the ancestral ape. I see clearly, however, that one mutation without the others would have been a deadly embarrassment, a variation not only of no survival value, but constituting even an enfeeblement. A change in the position of the skull in relation to the spinal column, involving a muscular reorganization of vision, but with no provision in feet or hands for the new mode of life, would produce a limping ape rather than a fleet-footed man. And what difficulties would be produced in the ape which had hands for manipulation and feet for running but was embarrassed by a skull and spinal structure which kept it on all fours! And how difficult it is to see all this happening, even through those leisurely aeons which the palaeontologists speak of as though they were simply last year's wet Sunday afternoons! If it is urged that nevertheless the Australopithecine shows features intermediary between man and ape, particularly in skull shape and position of the foramen magnum, then one is compelled to answer that it died out. Indeed, since 'from the neck down, modern man differs in no visible anatomic way from either Pithecanthropus or Rhodesian Man'[1]—and it is only in the union of the bodily features which he has in common with these creatures, with a large, a *double* brain that man is unique—it seems perfectly easy to assume the simultaneous emergence of Homo Sapiens with all the half men and ape men he resembles but who have since died out.

Even so, it is difficult to fit true man into the pattern of natural selection. It is unwise to assume that the acquisition of a large brain was an immediate survival advantage. As Professor Coon points out, 'the enlargement of the association area which went with an increase in the total brain size slowed down the learning process of the youthful primate, and increased the length of time the infant was obliged to remain dependent on its parents. The baby chimpanzee learns more rapidly than a human child until the time arrives when the human infant has begun to talk, and thus to learn primarily by speech stimuli rather than by visual stimuli. The more simply an animal lives the sooner it needs to be relieved of the care of its young, and

[1] Ibid., p. 36.

the sooner its young needs to be able to shift for itself. Man did not permanently acquire a full-sized brain until he had gone far enough along the cultural path to be able to nurse his big-brained children, who must have seemed to him slow and stupid, long enough to permit their survival into maturity.'[1] If one considers how the scales were weighted against man the wonder is that he survived. He was incapable of taking to the trees and brachiating like his cousins the apes and monkeys. He was confined to the ground. His physique was poorer than that of the larger animals by which he was surrounded, so that he could not hope to overcome them in a fight by his own unaided strength. He could not tear either his prey or his meat with his teeth as well as other animals, nor could he use his teeth very successfully in the place of tools. He lacked fur and therefore had little protection against extremes of heat and cold, the attacks of insects and parasites, and no protection against infection. In addition to all these disadvantages he was burdened with offspring which for the first year or eighteen months of life had to be carried everywhere, which were incapable for just about as long a time of feeding themselves, and indeed could not become economically independent until perhaps the tenth year, and which for the first three or four years were too feeble to protect themselves, even by flight. How so encumbered in that bitter, friendless, ancient world did the first man survive?

We have no clue unless we ask how the anthropologist defines man. And he does not know how to do this on purely physical grounds. All the creatures we have been considering are variations in a physical sense about an anthropoid type. If we were making a judgment about them from the standpoint of a different phylum we should speak of them all as allied animal species —members of one family. But we are involved in this case in the process of classifying ourselves. This family includes, physiologically speaking, many creatures like ourselves, and to decide which among them are men, we have to ask which of them are able to do the things we are able to do: for to us it is not simply the physical inheritance which makes us men, but the inheri-

[1] Ibid., p. 17.

70

tance of language, tools, techniques, art, religion, spiritual life and so forth, and were we to find a group of beings which possessed our physical make-up but lacked all these things we should have to decide that they were not men. 'The line dividing man and apes is so arbitrary that considerations other than anatomical features have to be taken into account; we are forced to fall back on defining man as a tool-maker, or as having the power of speech. We depend on his mental attributes more than on the shape of his bones. Since it is difficult to assess these qualities in fossils many thousands of years old, the subjective element creeps in unavoidably; the first physical anthropologist to describe a fossil, names it according to the resemblances or differences he sees in it with regard to known forms. . .'[1] Which is to say that we look at man backwards, down from the present rather than up from the past: to find man we look for a creature which speaks, which makes tools, and which has physically the attributes of a man. An anthropologist is probably going to have to make an inspired guess as to whether a creature with such and such a brain capacity could have had speech and could have made tools (if tools are not to be found with its remains) and though the most cunning, patient and exhaustive researches of the anthropologists yield continually new and surprising results, we must never forget the difficulty, perhaps the impossibility, of looking back across the abyss of centuries and deciding at what moment true man appears, and it can never be done without cultural evidence.

Sir Wilfred Le Gros Clark has said that 'probably the differentiation of man from ape will ultimately have to rest on a functional rather than on an anatomical basis, the criterion of humanity being the ability to speak and to make tools.' And Kenneth Oakley (in *Man the Toolmaker*) speaks of man as a social animal, 'distinguished by "culture": by the ability to make tools and communicate ideas. Employment of tools appears to be his chief biological characteristic.[2] Indeed, it is much more by the evidence of man's stone tools, with their different schools and styles and distributions, that the anthro-

[1] *The Prehistory of East Africa*, p. 64.   [2] Op. cit., London, 1956, p. 1.

pologists trace the whole prehistory of man through Palaeolithic
to Neolithic and finally to Bronze Age man. Fossil remains of
early man, as we have seen, are extremely rare, but the early
artifacts of men have been discovered in extraordinary abundance and studied and classified with minute care. They form
the chief stock of evidence about early human technical progress.

Man, therefore, is a cultural phenomenon, not a physical one.
The anatomical and physiological differences between man and
the other members of the Hominoidea are too slight for one to
say *physically* that here was an ape, and there was man. It seems
to be the simple truth that one of many apelike types was picked
out, or called out, to be man. At the moment that he appears as
man he is also in possession of a culture, and this though he may
be technically abject and poverty stricken, for it must be em-
phasized that the culture is never *purely* technical. The tool-
making capacity is of the utmost importance, of course, and I
shall return to it. In his capacity to make tools man reveals a
capacity for foresight which other intelligent members of his
own group do not posess. The work of Professor Köhler on the
habits of chimpanzees has revealed an interesting capacity on
the part of these apes to improvise tools and gadgets for emergencies visibly exposed to them. But they lack the capacity to
conceive a *future* emergency for which the present creation of a
tool will serve. They lack equally the power to reconstruct imaginatively in the probable future a situation in the past which
they have already encountered and conquered. It is not simply
that the band of awareness is narrower: there is a total in-
capacity for that kind of insight we call conceptual thinking.
There is no machinery for manipulating imaginatively even the
remembered experiences. As Kenneth Oakley writes, 'the systematic making of tools'—for activities which of course remain
in the future—'implies a marked capacity for conceptual
thought.'

The capacity to make tools seems, however, only a part of an
awakening to a new, and to the animal kingdom, undreamt of
realm. There are living societies of men which throw light upon

the enigma of technical poverty side by side with cultural richness. The Australian aborigines and the African bushmen are
Stone Age men. They move in a primitiveness beyond civilized
comprehension, owning few possessions, and boasting the
feeblest techniques, poorer in some things possibly than the
Java man, yet rich in a social and, of its kind, deeply religious
life. I think it is Spencer and Gillen who speak, in one of their
monumental studies of the Australian primitive, of a tribe whose
sole permanent possession was a bar of iron. It had neither
clothes nor dwellings nor tools: it was a drifting herd of food-
gatherers of poor physique with a standard of living a herd of
hogs would reject. Yet even so it enjoyed a rich tribal life of
ceremonial, initiations, *rites de passage*, and pious care of ancestral bones. How had it come by these things? How had it
moved away from the biological unit of organization, the
family, or from the animal hunting band, into a richly emotional, and closely knit artificial thing called a society? For the
economic poverty ought not to delude us. In appearance, and
in economic standards, it was a mere herd, but in social and
political life it was as rigidly organized as a regiment of soldiers.
If in such a destitute and denuded rabble of humanity which
could leave no trace of itself upon the earth but its bones we
find nevertheless a life brimming with the spiritual, it is a re-
minder of how careful we must be not to make rash assump-
tions about the sub-humanity of the earliest Homo Sapiens
simply on the basis of a material or technical poverty.

It is even thrilling to find in so poor a people, whose status in
so many things seems inferior to that of the animal, that there
is such an elaborate social life, that there are clearly organized
totemic groups, systems of relationships of the utmost subtlety,
codes of permissible marriage, betrothals conducted according
to rigid conventions, side by side with sharp age groupings and
initiations which mark the removal from one group to another,
and that the aborigines speak a complex language, and have
the capacity to write meaningful tribal symbols of great beauty,
and that there are ceremonies, sometimes orgiastic, but always
elaborate and significant, which are meant to imprint deeply

upon the minds of young and old the tribal form, the tribal identity, the tribal separateness. In a people which goes naked and scrapes holes in the sand to sleep—what is it all for, what purposes do these vast and economically unproductive expenditures of social energy serve?

The Guaharibos of the Orinoco, a people as we have seen possibly even more primitive than the aborigines of Australia, were visited by Alain Gheerbrant and his party in 1949. An account of this heroic exploit is given in *The Impossible Adventure*. His stay among them was brief and he was not in a position to conduct a full-scale anthropological research. However, he saw enough to convince him that here was a people which had barely moved away from the animal. The poverty of the encampment he stayed in was sickening. The huts were no more than ruined shelters made by leaning branches one against another. The population was spectral—pale, emaciated, diseased. The Guaharibos possessed neither hatchets nor knives, nor any tool-making techniques of importance, though they did boast bows and arrows. 'To fell a single tree is a more difficult undertaking for them than to raze a whole forest is for us. The only tool they have invented is what the Maquiritares contemptuously call "the Guaharibo knife"; it consists of a small piece of wood with an agouti tooth lashed to one end of it.'[1] Yet in the desolating encampment of naked savages under a three hundred feet high canopy of forest Gheerbrant was moved compassionately to see in these primitive people 'all signs of a reality as absolutely human as our own. He was particularly moved by the sorcerer whom he witnessed in the dead of night crouched over a fire smoulder, 'scattering into the night, words I could not understand, but whose alarm and appeal I could sense . . .

'As the Guaharibo sorcerer squatted there by his glowing hearth amidst the sleeping men, women, and children of his tribe and intoned his hurried invocations, a fire burnt in his own belly. Inside him was a small sun and he identified himself with the fire before him. He was the receptacle and the guardian

---

[1] Op. cit., p. 340.

of the flame by which his people grew and multiplied. He exor-
cised. He laboured. He wrestled with the monstrous forces of
the unknown which crowded in on him . . . The little sun in his
vitals, like the one that burnt at his feet, was his sole weapon: it
preserved and quickened life. He chanted there to secure the
future of mankind . . . Over thousands and thousands of square
miles of country, between sorrow and laughter, the life of naked
man advanced slowly and almost imperceptibly, between heat
and cold, good and evil, around such little men who chanted at
the centre of their stars.'[1]

If these are the most primitive people (and not simply degenerates created by the denseness and hostility of the prolific
Amazonian forests within which their superior enemies confined
them as in a prison), then here too a certain human situation
is complete. They are not animals. They possess speech of their
own, and could learn another, they make some tools and structures, they submit to a tribal order, they sing songs, they burn
their dead upon great bonfires and smear the ashes upon the
living to bring tribal increase, they seek to command or to conciliate the universe through their sorcerers. The Guaharibo,
Alain Gheerbrant writes, is the first man: one who sleeps curled
in on himself like a foetus in his damp cell. But still, the first
man and not the last animal.

The fully human phase of evolution did not begin, we are told
by the experts, until perhaps a quarter of a million years ago.
If that is so then we must say that we can still see peoples *in
every phase of that evolution,* from the most primitive to the most
advanced, if the reports of such explorers as Alain Gheerbrant
are to carry weight. When the stage of population expansion of
the species Homo Sapiens was reached, there was a deployment
of man eventually all over the world. Professor Carleton Coon
speaks of a first phase limited to the warmer lands of the Old
World, and of competing species of 'two-legged, two-handed
ground-living animals of the primate family'. In this first phase,
such experts say, man had already learnt to make tools and
probably to speak. In phase two, this creature colonized the

[1] Ibid., p. 345.

globe. In doing so, Homo Sapiens remained one species, capable everywhere of interbreeding and of cultural intercourse. By what power did this physically inferior creature accomplish his conquest of the world, and in doing so avoid the evolutionary tendency, which we are told is constant, to that increasing specialization which produces new species? There is no answer on the physiological plane at all: there is only a tentative answer on the cultural level. But the cultural level itself is not something we can in any way take as a natural evolutionary development. It is much more like one of Lloyd Morgan's 'emergents'—that is, something which could not be predicated from what had gone before. Culture is something new, something surprising. It is even more new and surprising than the emergence of creatures from the sea, or the spectacular leap of birds into the air. It is the exploration and colonization of a new territory, only it is not a physical territory any longer, but a spiritual one, and therefore invisible. It is reasonable to argue that man's conquest of the globe comes, despite his poor physique, because the new realm he enters gives him insight into, and promises him control over, the natural realm he has just left.

CHAPTER 4

The Tribal Identity

In *The Open Society* Karl Popper speaks of the 'closed' society, which for him can be magical or tribal or collectivist, as 'justly compared to an organism'. He thinks that the organic or biological theory of the state can be applied to it, and that the herd or the tribe is at least a semi-organic society the members of which are 'held together by semi-biological ties—kinship, living together, sharing common efforts, common dangers, common joys and common distress'.[1] It is arguable that this list is just as applicable to the most abstract and impersonal of open societies, and is therefore not a very useful one, but that point need not detain us, for the important argument is that the tribal society is somehow an organic one. It is close to the assertion of Sir Arthur Keith that the tribe 'is a "corporate body" which nature has entrusted with an assortment of human seed or genes, the assortment differing in some degree from that entrusted to every other tribe. If the genes are to work out their evolutionary effects, then it is necessary that the tribe or corporation should maintain its integrity through an infinity of generations.'[2] One recalls in this connection that Sir Arthur Keith believes the gene to be a purposive element in itself. In that case the tribe must be a body through which Nature works her will whether the parts of the body are aware of it or not.

[1] Op. cit., Vol. I, p. 173.
[2] *Essays on Human Evolution*, p. 5.

77

Now it is true that there are distinct tribal differences to be met with among primitive peoples and that one element in tribal solidarity is the sense of strong physical similarity and resentment of, or hostility towards, those of different physique or appearance. This is even now the most powerful element in the racial strife from which the world still suffers. Yet it is also true that tribes are often simply local sub-divisions of a larger people, or folk-group, also all physically alike, and that an infinite variety of relations may come into being among that people. The social life of the whole people may be patterned for instance upon the most elaborate totemic system, deriving its authority from the same religious or priestly background, transcending the tribe, in which case inter-marriage on a wide scale may not simply be tolerated but openly encouraged as necessary to the tribal health and to the economic well-being of a whole region. One can discover on the other hand peoples of the same breed or race, and therefore of the same physical appearance, divided into tribes which are mutually exclusive and even normally at war, and in which from time to time a pattern of relationships will arise in which the victorious tribe will dominate others in a fashion which we can describe as imperialist. When that imperialism involves inter-marriage with the conquered, then obviously the tribal gene has been told to go and hang itself. One has only to consider the relationships of the tribes of Israel, or of our own Anglo-Saxon forebears, or of the ancient Greeks, or of contemporary raiding Bedouin to see that no simple argument based on the authority of the genes is a sufficient explanation of tribal existence. One can discover infinite gradations of relations from tribal exclusiveness, to inter-tribal co-operation, including such institutions as inter-tribal gatherings for the purpose of promiscuous sexual intercourse in order, to borrow Sir Arthur Keith's language, deliberately to mix the genes Nature intended to keep unmixed. In fact, the argument that the tribe has its origins in a search for racial purity breaks down just as emphatically at the truly tribal level as at the level of Hitler's Germany. One has only to remember (at the tribal, not at the German level) the widespread practice of offering the friendly visitor, even though of quite different race and colour, the choice of tribal women to sleep with, to see that the biological exclusiveness has probably always taken a level below that which we might call cultural integrity. The stealing of women from other tribes is as old as tribal life itself, and there are very few primitive peoples in which traces of inter-marriage with other racial groups are not to be detected at some time or another. It also seems probable that a distinct tribal identity in a *physical* sense could only come into existence after many generations of inbreeding. It would not be a characteristic possessed by a tribe at the beginning of its tribal history. If that is true the distinguishing physical appearance of a tribe would be the product of its cultural separateness, rather than the reverse.

Of course there is a difference between Sir Arthur Keith's argument that the tribe is a guardian of certain genes, and the argument of Professor Popper that the tribe is a kind of organism. The first argument makes it possible to say that the social or cultural life has a biological or genetic significance. The second argument is that the tribe is a kind of animal body, and its social and cultural functions are merely a by-product of the biological functions. I am afraid both are fallacious ways of thinking. Of course, biological functions are fulfilled within a tribal society; but so they are within a civilized or open society. This is not sufficient ground to justify describing either society as organic. An organism at the level of complexity which would justify comparison with a society, is a psycho-somatic whole. It is the originator, co-ordinator and user of its several parts: without the psycho-somatic whole no parts would ever come into existence. It would be absurd to argue this of human society at any kind of level. Indeed, the contrary is true. In human society it is the parts which bring the society into existence for their purposes. They maintain it, modify it, transform it, even abolish it if it fails to suit their needs. Human history is full of examples of how men have survived the destruction of their most cherished institutions and political forms, and gone on biologically functioning nevertheless. It is impossible to imagine the parts of any highly developed organism surviving the destruction of the unity of the whole.

The nearest analogy to the human situation in the animal kingdom is the insect society. Insect societies are based upon a high degree of sexual and economic specialization, and the major undertaking of the society is to do collectively for its members what they have ceased to be individually capable of doing for themselves. Individual powers are lost in insect societies—so far that irrevocable somatic modifications take place which deprive the mass of the members of the society even of the power to reproduce. The differentiation which takes place makes it possible to argue that each separate insect is in some sense a 'cell', and that the whole anthill is the body, the organism, even though this is flying in the face of the visual evidence. The dependence of the individual insect on the society is close to the dependence of cells on the functions of the total organism. Yet the parallel must not be pressed too far, for the ant colony behaves in many ways like a true association, a true collective, rather than as a true organism: in the collecting and growth of food, for example, or in war. Individual insects appear to vary in enterprise and excitability, as well as in function: they vary, that is, as individuals vary. The most enterprising insects lead forays which result in extensions of the ant 'lebensraum', and increases in in its food supplies. They communicate their finds, insect to insect, as a collective must, but as the cells of a body do not need to do. Some insects exhibit a greater sense of social responsibility, and others show less, just as men do; some are energetic, some are lazy. Some explore, others do not. Indeed, one cannot study the ant colony without gathering awareness that this is a social enterprise, not simply a biological one. But it is plainly false to describe it as an organism.[1]

How less easy it is then to speak of *human* societies in organic terms! The insect society has a biological corporateness (but not a body) but it has no history, it has no continuing social consciousness, no apparent awareness of what it is repeating and why. It is fast fixed within the natural cycle in which it revolves

[1] Cf. Derek Wragge Morley, *The Ant World*, London, 1953, pp. 171 et seq.

indefinitely and obliviously without addition or subtraction. Bird communities and animal communities exhibit a happy gregariousness arising from a common way of life. The habit of flocking or herding tells us that creatures of the same species, and sometimes even of dissimilar species, find great satisfaction and a sense of security in herding together. But all this goes on without history, without any continuous social consciousness, without the accumulation of experience. If man has a natural community in the animal sense, it is the family, or the loose horde or band into which a family might easily develop. There is perhaps every reason why that horde should remain together even after the infant members of the original family have attained maturity. The natural gregariousness of man would explain the desirability though not the economic practicability of this loose association. What is impossible to conceive in purely natural terms is why such a family, or group of families, or horde of like beings should ever develop the structured society which we recognize as a tribe, exercising a firm but invisible discipline over its members, even over those members which have passed puberty and are by nature therefore fully equipped to go off and found independent families of their own.

As a matter of fact, seventeenth and eighteenth century thinkers found it inconceivable that the most primitive state of mankind was anything else but a state of complete individual independence. For Hobbes and Locke and Rousseau, man in a state of nature was free and sovereign. He was under no man's rule, and subject to no tribe's tyranny. And the atomization of primitive mankind in this way was to them such an inescapable human birthright that the real difficulty was to show why man ever surrendered his animal freedom and gave to society that dangerous sovereignty over his life and liberty which had once been his private gift from God and which society anyway so often and so openly abused. These thinkers disagreed as to the nature of the inducements which caused man to surrender his liberty, but they were at one in describing society as an artificial contrivance of man, and not as the given basis of man's humanity.

Sigmund Freud saw this problem and discussed it in *Totem*

F   81

and Tabu: inevitably in a sexual context. In most animal societies, gregariousness is greatest during periods of sexual quiescence: perhaps the flocking of birds in the autumn and winter is the best example of this. Once the herd or flock wakens from its sexual sleep, then some atomization of the flock takes place. The bird flocks of many species entirely disappear and in their place we find the multitude of bird pairs whose loyalty is only to their nest and broods and who are at enmity with other pairs. The sexual urges are too great to permit the tolerance necessary to keep the flock in existence; the flock itself is possibly also the economic enemy of the family group. But with man there is no close sexual season—no time therefore when gregariousness is less dangerous or explosive than others. And Freud saw that if society with all its prohibitions, disciplines and taboos, many of them strongly sexual, had come into existence against so to speak the powerful but anarchic sexual urges of the young male, then there had really to be a unique explanation for an event so contrary to nature. And Freud knew of no urge greater than the sexual urge, and he could not justify so remarkable a repression of man's sexuality at the behest of society except in terms of the explanation habitual to him, that the same energy which was the source of man's sexual drive could be turned into a sexual brake.

To Freud's argument I shall recur. But what I have so far said must have made it clear that—if we except the insects which have been physiologically adapted to the servile life of the insect state—no animal in a wild state is prepared to submit voluntarily to the will of another, or to endure any limitations to the exercise of its natural powers and functions save those which necessity imposes. It refuses the prohibitions I spoke of in the preface. If there is food, it will eat: if not, it cannot. If it is on heat, it will mate, if there is a partner: if not, it cannot. If food is available, or if a mate is available, and anything seeks to restrain it, it will fight. Man alone chooses another way. Only man, while establishing control over natural things, unnaturally surrenders rights over his life and liberties to the society into which he is born.

As to how this potentially sovereign natural being, who has the example of his cousins of the Hominoidea to show him how he might naturally behave, is able to turn upon the nature with which he is endowed and subdue it or crush it, that, as the social contract theorists saw, is indeed an enigma. I may be excused from seeking to unravel it at this point, I think; but if it is uncertain how it is done, we do know precisely *what* has to be done. It is what Hobbes tells us about in *Leviathan*. Man has to give his allegiance to something other than his natural gifts and impulses. He must step outside nature into another frame of reference, a frame which in contrast with nature is going to be artificial—for this other frame is not a birthright, but in a sense is at first completely unknown, and grasped at with difficulty and constructed and maintained with infinite pain and endless labour. It is the ledge above which man struggles to reach, and when he reaches it, its vantage-point enables him to see things below him in another perspective and to recognize *the separation which has taken place and which has lifted him out of nature*, a separation he seeks by all means in his power to perpetuate.

It is certainly true that no known tribe is satisfied simply with that distinction which its private pattern of genes awards it. The natural physique is not enough, and every human group seeks its own style to enhance or transform its original endowments. The artificial decorations may be woad or paint or clothes, head-dresses, armbands, necklaces, girdles, weapons and the other endless contrivances of humanity for the better display of their own bodies; or they may be cosmetic activities, like depilation, shaving, hairdressing, and the oiling of the skin; or they may be physical mutilation. If we look first at some circumcision rites and what they involve we may better understand the intention of these activities.

In one of their monumental tomes, Spencer and Gillen discuss the initiation rites of the northern tribes of Central Australia for boys at or approaching puberty.[1] These are not the only initiation ceremonies of these tribes. Some of the coastal

[1] Spencer and Gillen, *Northern Tribes of Central Australia*, London, 1906.

83

tribes practise the knocking out of one or more of the upper incisor teeth. They speak too of a tribe, the Lakaria, in the country near Port Darwin, which practised yet another form of initiation. The youths who had arrived at the age of puberty were taken away and isolated by the old men of the tribe, and subjected to rude buffets and tests. Blows were aimed at them, or food kept from them, or they were set to climb, or fell large trees, or to swim in crocodile-infested rivers, and to endure these humiliations and dangers without grumbling. Only at the end, when this initiation was safely accomplished, were the youths shown the tribal bull-roarer, whose voice women believed to be that of a spirit which came down from the sky and took the youths away into the bush from which they were to return initiated men. And even the most painful and cruel initiations practised by these savages maintained a similar element of sacredness.

In the Urunna tribe, we are told, when the time has come for the boy's initiation, his paternal grandfather seizes hold of him and after some ceremonies before the women which are meant to mark him as an initiate, he goes upon a journey with his mentor, rather like a *chela* with his *guru*, visiting different groups and inviting them to the ceremony. Upon this journey the persons of the boy and his guardian are sacred and may not be attacked by fellow tribesmen. Upon their return there follow several nights of ceremonies before the boy is finally circumcised by the elderly male relatives tradition assigns to the task. He is taken away into the bush and kept *incommunicado* until he has recovered, and then brought back and immediately, with as much ceremony, sub-incised. When this is over, he is shown, on the same night, more sacred totemic ceremonies, and the elderly male relatives who have supervised the initiation tell him that he is now a man and not a boy. He must not attempt intercourse with *lubras* other than his lawful wives, and he is not on any account to interfere with the lubras belonging to other men. If he breaks the taboos he will fall down dead like the stones. Only after all this may he sit in the men's camp, and take a wife to himself.

A deeply sympathetic observer of the aborigine, Charles P. Mountford, describes the ceremony of tribal expulsion in this vivid fashion. 'One evening . . . the happy, carefree life of one of their number is completely shattered. Closely related women, his source of comfort in every childish trouble, suddenly attack him, and, with blazing firesticks, drive him from the camp. By that ceremonial expulsion the lad is deprived of the affection and indulgence of the women, and forced to live under the dominance of the gruff, unresponsive old men, his tutors on the long difficult road to tribal manhood. From then, until the circumcision ceremonies are completed, perhaps in a year or so, the youth is treated as an outcast. He always sleeps at some distance from the main camp; never goes near or calls out to the women; nor does he speak to the old men unless first addressed, and then his reply must not be above a whisper. It is a most drastic break, and the youth must be thoroughly puzzled and distressed over the many prohibitions that have so quickly surrounded him . . . Eventually the day comes when he is pounced upon by the old men, and, to the accompaniment of the wailing of the women and the shouting and stamping of the already initiated men, he is led to the *secret grounds*.

'During the initiation rituals the men who stand in close relationship to him open the veins in their arms and allow the blood to pour over his body. The fundamental idea behind this custom is that blood is *kuranita* (life essence), and the giving of ample supplies of blood will provide the initiate with the necessary health and vitality to grow to strong and virile manhood.'[1]

The ceremonies of some tribes are of infinite complication, but in the main what is common to them all is that the boy is taken away from the women's camp in a ceremonial fashion which marks the end of his childhood, he is shown to those tribal groups which should attend the ceremony, he is brought back to sacred grounds normally taboo to women, and there ceremonies are endlessly performed within his hearing though not always within his sight. The dances and ceremonial plays

[1] *Brown Men and Red Sand*, London, 1950, pp. 44-5.

and displays may go on for several days, before the dazed child
is circumcised: the moment when this will occur is normally
hidden from him, and he cannot know what to expect, save that
he may be put to death and brought to life again by the tribal
or totemic spirit, as the women will have warned him. The
initiation may include mock attacks on him with spears; but as
no initiate ever reveals to those younger what he passes through,
he does not know that one of those spears will not presently
pierce him. When the ceremony is over, and only then, his
sacred totem or totem sign will be revealed to him, and it is
made known that he is now a man and can sit with the men and
take a wife. The awfulness of the ceremonies is increased by the
magical use of blood, in the manner Charles P. Mountford has
pointed out; but then blood from the boy's own wounds may
also be used ritually—it may be given to the mother and father
to drink, or sucked by the youth from the knife which cut him,
or smeared on the backs of the officiating old men. In many
tribes it is regarded as dreadful for the blood to be allowed to
fall to the ground.

Spencer and Gillen said of the initiation ceremonies: 'We
tried in vain to find any satisfactory explanation of the ceremonies of circumcision and sub-incision, but so far as we could
discover the native has no idea whatever of what these ceremonies mean . . . and it is rather a curious fact that they have
not invented some tradition to explain their meaning'.[1] However, John Layard, in *The Stone Men of Malekula: Vao*, describing
the elaborate ceremonies of the New Hebrides, said that the
mutilation or removal of the foreskin represented a departure
from nature which was 'liable to call down the wrath of nature'.
In its cultural aspect it is a sign of manhood and of man's ability,
through sacrifice, to conquer nature, expressed in the phrase
that till a youth is incised he is "only a woman".'[2]

The best evidence of the purpose of circumcision in the eyes
of tribal peoples of all kinds is the passage in Genesis, where the
Lord declares: 'This is my covenant, which ye shall keep, be-

[1] *The Northern Tribes of Central Australia*, p. 330.
[2] *The Stone Men of Malekula*, London, 1942, p. 481.

tween me and you and thy seed after thee; every male among you shall be circumcised. And ye shall be circumcised in the flesh of your foreskin; and it shall be a token of a covenant betwixt me and you. And he that is eight days old shall be circumcised among you, every man child throughout your generations, he that is born in the house, or bought with money of any stranger, which is not of the seed. He that is born in thy house, and he that is bought with thy money, must needs be circumcised; and my covenant shall be in your flesh for an everlasting covenant. And the uncircumcised man child whose flesh of his foreskin is not circumcised, that soul shall be cut off from his people; he hath broken my covenant.'[1]

The Jews were the most profoundly religious people the world has ever seen, and it was impossible for them to conceive of circumcision outside their relationship with God. And so in that proud statement, pregnant with remorseless purpose, circumcision is declared the seal of God in the flesh of man. Those who have it not shall be cast out. There could hardly be a more remarkable example of circumcision as a badge of tribal identity. And because it is a badge, not a personal initiation, it is important to perform it in infancy rather than at puberty when its significance might be confused by its association with the emergence of sexual powers. It is not the only badge we can find. Among some African tribes the last joint of the little finger is chopped off. Cave-drawings in France show Stone Age men with precisely the same mutilation. The Maoris tattooed their bodies in intricate and beautiful patterns. The Nuer peoples of the Nile cut a deep scar across the forehead of the young initiates: marks of it are found even upon the skulls of the dead. The Piorias of the Orinoco dope the initiates with drink and drugs and draw over their bodies webs of fierce stinging ants, then beat the children in the village square. Many African tribes practise scarification, again in elaborate patterns of aesthetic and social significance. The Eskimos file their teeth, to make them less like those of dogs. The piercing of the septum, the wearing of nose rings and earrings, the deforma-

[1] Chap. 17, v. 10-14.

tion of the skull, or of the bones of the neck, or of the genital organs—there is almost no end to the deliberate and distinctive mutilations or decorations of the body associated with tribal recognition. And in very many cases these other mutilations are practised side by side with circumcision, cliterodectomy, and sub-incision.

It is the remarkable popularity of circumcision among primitive peoples that compels one to ask whether it has greater significance than simply to act as a badge of tribal recognition, and the hoary antiquity of the practice was perhaps revealed unconsciously by Spencer and Gillen when they said that the natives could not account for it, and had not even invented a myth or story to justify it. That seems to make it as much a matter of course to them as the air they breathed, so much taken for granted as part of the tribal order that explanation was considered unnecessary. Of course, there have been other explanations. One is that circumcision masks the castration threat. Sigmund Freud has associated circumcision with anti-semitism, seeking to explain that people unconsciously become anti-semitic because circumcision is associated in their minds with the threat against male virility. The argument generally, I suppose, is that the youth at puberty becomes the rival of the old males of the tribe, and circumcision is simply what is left of the threat (or perhaps practice) of castration of the sexually anarchic young males. In that case circumcision is simply a substitute for castration as animal sacrifice is sometimes a substitute for human sacrifice. This is at once too simple and too sophisticated an explanation. It overlooks first that the dominant tribal element, even in those aboriginal tribes we have been considering, consists of the *old* men, jealous guardians of the tribal mores and tribal existence: they, the sexually spent, would have been less deeply affected by sexual rivalry of the boys than would be the young male in his prime. It is a necessary part of the tribal system that the old males should triumph politically and socially over the young bulls of the tribes, as well as over the impotent children. The youth at puberty is less able, sexually and economically, to challenge the old men of the

88

tribe than is the male in his prime. It is against the male in his prime, if against anyone, that the old male would have been justified in launching his castration threat. And then too, why castration? Why not, simply, murder? Primitive peoples do not shrink from murder, and murder would have been simpler and more successful than leaving a useless and conceivably revengeful tribal eunuch to sour the tribal life. But there is no evidence at all of the practice of castration in primitive tribes, except of dead male enemies as a sign of triumph. And I think too, that anthropologists have disposed of the idea that circumcision and sub-incision have any relation to a wish to restrict population by some kind of birth control. It is a remedy which would never occur, in any case, to primitive people who do not associate sexual intercourse with pregnancy, or who, if they do, yet believe that the entry of the ancestral spirit into the womb of the mother is at least as essential an element in conception as copulation, and may occur independently of the sexual act. Such views may have been more widespread among primitive peoples than they are now. Besides, as Spencer and Gillen say, what simpler remedy to hand than infanticide, which is still practised and was known throughout antiquity?

Among primitive peoples, where circumcision is practised at or near puberty, it is certainly not regarded as a punishment, but as a sign of virility, and of acceptance into the tribal maleness. It is the uncircumcised boy who is jeered at as a woman, and made the object of general mockery. In African tribes it is the uncircumcised one who is the irresponsible one, free to break tribal taboos, defiance of which would strike his elders down dead. Indeed, the act of circumcision is the entry into, not the threat of deprival of, male sexual privileges. In *The Origins and History of Consciousness* Erich Neumann writes that the initiations and 'the trials of endurance are tests of the virility and stability of the ego; they are not to be taken personalistically as "the vengeance of the old" upon the young, any more than our matriculation is the vengeance of old men upon the rising generation, but merely a certificate of maturity for entry into the collective. In almost all cases, age brings an in-

crease in power and importance based on the increased knowledge gained through successive initiations, so that the old men
have little case for resentment'.[1] Neumann links the specifically
male initiations not with sexual or genital rôles at all, but with
the rise of the *assertive male consciousness*. They are the mark of its
liberation from the matriarchate. Male self-assertion, so manifest in those male initiations from which women are excluded
on pain of death, and which may not even be reported to them,
is a witness to the birth of a higher consciousness in man, of an
intellectual and managerial capacity which deliberately cuts
itself off from the intuitive and generally blurring female consciousness, a male power only capable of coming to birth when
the tie with the female consciousness is broken. 'The higher
masculinity here in point has no phallic or chthonic accent; its
content is not, as in many initiations of young girls, sexuality,
but its counterpole, spirit, which appears together with light,
the sun, the head, and the eye as symbols of consciousness. This
spirit is what is accentuated, and into it the initiations lead'.[2]

I accept in general this argument. However, for entry into
the male circle or the tribal collective any systematic initiation
would serve, and obviously does serve, for we know not all
initiations involve circumcision, and many are performed on
what is sometimes spoken of as man's secondary or higher
sexuality—his head. Nevertheless the universality of circumcision and its relation to the genitalia, make it specially significant, for the more widespread its use the less effective it is as a
badge of recognition whether in the Scriptural or the tribal
sense. It must then be significant in other ways. And here one
may venture one or two observations.

Circumcision is generally, though not always, performed
around puberty. It has therefore a very special sexual pointing.
It is a painful operation, associated with the advent of sexual
powers, *but imposed by the tribe*. What must it serve to do in the

[1] Op. cit., London, 1954, p. 141.

[2] Ibid., pp. 141-2. For an eye-witness account of girls' initiation ceremonies among the Bemba of Northern Rhodesia, and their relation to
sexuality and marriage, the reader is referred to *Chisungu* by Audrey I.
Richards, London, 1956.

child mind? First, to make him feel that his sexual maturity is, in a sense, within the gift of the tribe; then, to deepen the awe and mystery which surround the generative powers; then, by the pain and misery temporarily inflicted upon him, to breed in him the consciousness that the tribe stands over the sexual powers, able by pain to subdue pleasure whenever it needs to. And this complex of ideas, made more vivid by the ceremonies themselves, marks the entry of the boy into the sphere of strict sexual taboos and marital and economic and political responsibilities, where sex can be no longer wholly play, indeed into the sphere where all its manifestations *at last* carry social consequences.

Of course, puberty is itself a physical transformation of a total kind. It produces a new being, and the passage through puberty brings with it the sense of being born into a new world and the 'death' of the child and the 'birth' of the man is an important part of all pubertal *rites de passage*. In the Poro Society of Liberia a most elaborate form of deception used to be practised: at the entrance to the ceremonial camp in which their circumcision and subsequent scarification would take place, and in which they would remain for three years, a ceremonial 'death' of the youths took place. 'In the old days they [the boys] were apparently run through with a spear and tossed over the curtain. Onlookers heard a thud as he [the boy] was supposed to hit the ground inside, dead. Actually, the boy was protected by a chunk of plantain stalk tied on under his clothes. Into this the spear was thrust. A bladder of chicken's blood at the right spot was punctured and spilled to make it all very realistic to other boys and women who could not resist the desire to see their sons, perhaps for the last time. Inside the fence [the officer] and two assistants, all masked, caught the boys in mid-air, and dropped a heavy dummy to complete the delusion. The boys were actually unharmed, and were quickly carried away into the deep forest which is the Poro grove.'[1]

[1] 'Notes on the Poro in Liberia' by Dr. George Harley. Peabody Museum Papers, vol. 19, no. 2. Cambridge, Mass., 1841. From *Reader in General Anthropology* by C. S. Coon, London, 1950, p. 359.

Even the subsequent painful scarifying ceremonies had a death and re-birth theme. The scars were supposed to be the marks of the great crocodile spirit which had swallowed the boys and in whose belly they had lived during their stay in the bush.

We have to recognize that all these ceremonies of initiation encounter a psychological resistance: the more painful they are, the greater the reluctance of the initiates to face them, and the greater the suffering of the parents and other adults at the pain they have to inflict. All such acts of mutilation have to take place against emotional shrinking: indeed much of their value arises out of the general resistance which has to be overcome. We cannot ourselves understand these things if we forget what it is to be human. When we are faced with unpleasant duties we tend to postpone them, or to find reasons for not doing them, or simply fail to remember them. This lazy postponement or actual forgetting must always have faced man in his tribal condition too. It is therefore important to realize that the ritual heightening of the ceremonies of initiation has precisely the intention of making the whole event tribally memorable and spiritually significant. Long preparatory rites and ceremonies and elaborate dances produce exaltation in initiates and participants alike. They launch the whole tribe or village or clan into a spiritual glissade which gathers momentum, and of which the climax is the painful mutilation of the young. And once launched upon the ceremonial cycle it presently becomes inconceivable that the whole drama should not mount to its great climax. Even the initiates become as sleepwalkers, carried on irresistibly by the great drama. In *The Dark Child* Camara Laye, a young negro from French Guinea, has written what must be the first account of what it means to be a tribal initiate in a book which is a minor literary masterpiece.

'It was not without misgivings that I approached this transition from childhood to manhood; the thought of it really caused me great distress, as it did those who were to share the ordeal . . . But however great the anxiety, however certain the pain, no one would have dreamed of running away from the ordeal—no more than one would have dreamed of running away from the ordeal of the lions—and I for my own part never entertained such thoughts. I wanted to be born, to be born again. I knew perfectly well that I was going to be hurt, but I wanted to be a man and it seemed to me that nothing could be too painful if, by enduring it, I was to come to man's estate. My companions felt the same; like myself, they were prepared to pay for it with their blood. Our elders before us had paid for it thus; those who were born after us would pay for it in their turn. Why should we be spared? Life itself would spring from the shedding of our blood.'[1]

There were two aspects of the ceremony, the public rejoicing and the secret initiation. In the public ceremony, the whole village was given over to noisy festival. For a whole week Camara and his companions, already lodged in a special enclosure, danced in the main square day after day the dance of those who are to be circumcised. 'Were we not dancing to forget what we were all dreading?' The whole town danced with them. 'In our country, all dances have this cumulative tendency, because each beat of the tom-tom has an almost irresistible appeal.'[2] Men, women and girls outdid the youths in frenzy. And then, after days of endless and exhausting dances, the specially clothed initiates were taken into the bush, into a sacred place. The old and famous 'operator' appeared with his knives, and in a few seconds, Camara Laye relates, the dozen or so boys 'became men'. The boys were shocked by the abundant flow of blood: only when it had more or less ceased could their wounds be dressed.

'When the blood had finally ceased flowing, we were dressed in our long *boubou* again. Apart from a very brief undershirt, this was to be our only article of attire during the weeks of convalescence that were to come. We stood up awkwardly, light-headed and sick at our stomachs. Among the men who had been present at the operation, I saw several who, taking pity on our plight, turned their heads away to hide their tears.'[3] The boys returned to the feast in their honour, the social climax of the

---

[1] Op. cit., London, 1955, pp. 112-13.   [2] Ibid., p. 114.
[3] Ibid., p. 125.

affair, but could not eat, for all had a touch of fever. Perhaps for days, in their strict seclusion, under ceaseless watch and nursing at the hands of special male attendants, they would have this fever. Not until three weeks had passed could Camara see his mother, nor until after four weeks was he allowed any liberty. The circumcised boys were obviously ritually taboo: but they were also medically isolated in order to speed up their recovery; for what indeed was inflicted upon them was much the same as a serious illness.

Some teaching accompanied the rite. The boys were commanded to be honest, to fulfil their duties towards God, and towards their parents and superiors, and to befriend their neighbours. There was nothing, the young man relates, not fit for other ears than their own. The moral tone was appropriate to a Christian Sunday School: and indeed it seems that this would also be true of the secret ethical instructions given to aboriginal initiates in Australia. Merely to impart such ethical instruction, so awesome and painful a ceremony was hardly necessary. No, the principal part of the ceremony was 'becoming men'. But the boys would have become men in the course of nature anyway, and so the passage into manhood marked by the ceremony was either gratuitous or else was much more than a guarantee of that which nature had in any case given them. The clue to the meaning of the ceremony is in the declaration which Camara makes of solidarity with the tribe—that he will be like them, and pass through the same ordeals, and pay for his tribal identity with his blood. It is, in fact, not the entry into manhood as such which the ceremony marks, but the entry into the realm where mere manhood or mere maturity has to be subordinated even through suffering to the demands of the tribe. That is to say it is not his natural but his social, or political person which was born. But that social and political person inherits a responsibility for a minutely structured society: in short, it is a *spiritual* inheritance into which the boy is born, an inheritance which from the very beginning carries its burden of pain and suffering, though these are not always of a physical nature.

There is, in one tribal history, an interesting association of circumcision with technical advances. It is told by Spencer and Gillen in a legend of the Kaitish aborigines:

'In the Alcheringa two eggs were laid in a nest at Unjuia, out of which came two Ullakuppera (little hawk) boys. The elder one broke through the shell first, and when he had come out he listened and heard the younger brother making a noise in his shell, so he broke it and set him free. The younger one coming out said, "Hullo, where is my father?" and the elder one said, "We have no father or mother." The younger one said, "Which way shall we walk, shall we go towards the Altimala (west)?" but the elder one merely stood up and said nothing. Then the younger one said, "Shall we walk towards the Okniroka (east)?" but the elder one did not reply for some time, and at last said, "We will walk to the Altranga (north)." Then they set off. As they went along they gradually increased in size until, when they reached a hill a little to the north of the Foster range, called Karrarinia, their pubic hairs were beginning to appear. All along the way they met with incomplete human beings called *inter-intera*, who, like the two boys, were continually trying to pull their foreskins back. Up in the sky there dwelt a great being called Atnatu, who had a black face and no *atna* (anus). Looking down he saw the two boys walking about searching for rats, and pulling their foreskins back in the hope of making themselves into young men. They went out on three or four successive days, and on the fifth the elder boy went out alone amongst the hills. To his surprise he saw what at first he thought was a big leaf tumbling down, but on catching it in his hands he found that it was a large *leilirra*—a stone knife—sent down by Atnatu. He at once circumcised himself with it and then returned to camp, where his younger brother on seeing him said, "Hullo, my big brother has been and cut himself." Then the younger brother went out into the bush, and once more Atnatu sent down a knife with which the boy cut himself and returned to camp, where the elder brother saw what had happened and said, "Hullo, my little brother has been and cut himself." Then the two sat down opposite each other and performed the rite of sub-incision, and the blood of the elder boy

95

flowed right away across the Barrow Creek flats, carving out a creek bed which still remains. It flowed on until it reached Urkampitjera, a spot some twenty miles away to the north. The blood of the younger boy flowed to the north-west, and made a little creek running down from the Foster Range to the north; then it went on to Kopertanda, where it spread out, made a waterhole, and flowed on. When they had thus transformed themselves into fully initiated men, the two, who were now grown-up men, walked about the country, performing the initiation rite upon different groups of men and women whom they met in the course of their travels. Amongst others they initiated some little bird people called *Lintjalinga*, whom they heard singing, and watched while they tried to circumcise themselves with a fire-stick . . .'[1]

The beautiful legend of the creation mission of the two brothers moves on with dignity to tell of their death by a waterhole. 'After a time the younger brother said, "You and I are tired, shall we kneel down?" but the elder brother made no reply. Then the younger knelt down with his hands behind him, and after a time he said, "Shall we stand up?" Still there was no reply from the elder. They were carrying their *leilirra* in their waist girdles, and had sacred *Churinga* [sacred stones] under their armpits, on their shoulders, and in their hands, pressed up close against their stomachs. At last the big brother spoke and said, "We will neither kneel nor stand, but will lie down here. If we kneel or stand our *Churinga* will be seen, and then the place will be *ekerinja* (tabooed), and all the black fellows will not be able to come and drink. Let us lie down upon them, and then they will not be able to be seen, and every one will be able to come and drink." So they lay down upon their *Churinga* and died, and two great stones arose to mark the spot'.[2]

I have the uncanny feeling that through this story we may be looking down through the great void of the past to the point where man's humanity is marked by the simultaneous arrival of stone knives and the circumcision which would be humanly

---

[1] *The Northern Tribes of Central Australia*, pp. 344-6.   [2] Ibid., p. 346.

impossible without them. It suggests that still more primitive people, possessing only fire-sticks, looked with envy upon those who had achieved a higher technical level and received missionaries from them. Circumcision marks therefore, if this assumption is a reasonable one, a stage in man's technical advance. Before the use of knives, man's hunting must have been restricted to the food gathering of small edible things—nuts, fruits, grubs, small game which could be eaten with the minimum of preparation. Large game was useless except in so far that it could be torn to pieces with the teeth and the hands—and we have already learnt that man was singularly poorly physically equipped for this. With fire, some larger game might be broken down to an edible stage, but the technical difficulties in the way of capturing, killing and dismembering larger creatures must have been almost insuperable. The first stone knife transformed that situation. It may have made possible killing large animals. It certainly made it possible to dismember them. And it is an advance of the highest order for intellectual reasons too. Knife in hand, primitive man becomes a crude surgeon. He skins his game and uses the skins. His knives dismember carcasses, separating parts, and he learns his first lessons in bodily structures. He exposes the most secret parts of entire creatures to his curious eyes and fingers. Perhaps it is on animals first that he learnt the primitive surgery he practised on his own kith and kin. But certainly the two advances came together; and when early man had learnt to use his knives he must have recognized how much they separated him from the animals, and how far advanced he was over peoples still more primitive, who did not yet possess them. This feeling is implicit in the story I have related. To circumcise would be to advertise this human superiority over the animal. That is why it was the mission of the two brothers to transform the various beings they met into 'complete' men, and initiate them by circumcision.

We must recognize, I think, that a sense of the sacredness of life breathes through this story of human origins. The behaviour of the two brothers, knowing death upon them, and contriving to die in such a manner that they would not deprive their brethren of water, is in the highest degree comradely and un-selfish, and movingly told. If we see in it man making his first technical advance, we see man already possessed of the highest degree of compassion.

When all that can be rationally said about circumcision, sub-incision and similar ceremonies has been said, we should be un-wise not to recognize something dark in these practices. I am not thinking here so much of the magical and demoniacal aspects of primitive ceremony, about which I will say something later, but about evil. There is a manifest love of cruelty in man, even self-inflicted cruelty, and the farther we go back in human history, the less it is disguised. It is certainly present in much primitive ceremony, especially, of course, in ceremonies of initiation. The conclusion has to be drawn that the tribal old men enjoy the pain they inflict—though not simply wantonly, for it is a stern social duty too. But in the revolting developments of repeated sub-incision which certain aboriginal peoples prac-tice, there is obviously an exploration of the possibilities of in-flicting pain. It is perhaps (so little do we understand our human condition) even a mark of unconscious human genius, that tribal ceremonies rigorize the cruelty that man wills to inflict even on those near and dear to him and provide a periodic surrogate for man's cruel lusts. But even that rigorizing can itself become the excuse for further cruelty—to understand this we have to recall the long record of human sacrifice in world history, particularly perhaps the endless butcheries practised by such as the Aztecs as part of the observance of religious rites.

Animals are not cruel: when we *say* that they are cruel we mean that they are ferocious—they will fight to survive, or to triumph, or to kill, when they have to, with an unfaltering will. But to be cruel they would need to identify themselves with their victims, and that they never do, so a fox or an otter wan-tonly killing, is simply working off an excess of killing fever. It has no enjoyment of anything but its own power. But the man inflicting pain on another is in spiritual sickness, for that which is obsessing him is what his victim is suffering. He is identifying himself with his victim all the time and loses interest when his victim loses consciousness. So that if we admit that there is a strange genius in the use of circumcision and similar rites of initiation in the solution of problems of tribal unity and identity, let us not endow savages with virtues of restraint and moderation sparse enough even among civilized peoples. In the very legend I have been quoting, the same *Atnatu* who showered upon men the gift of knives, in another story grew furious with men who failed to sound the bull-roarer loudly or sufficiently long, and hurled down his spears upon them, dragged them up into the sky, and ate one of them.

In the Scriptural narrative, as I pointed out, the institution of the rite of circumcision of the new-born was part of the covenant with God. Abraham marked it by the circumcision of the whole male portion of his household, from the infant Isaac upwards. It is followed immediately in the Bible story—and significantly, I think—by the visit of the three angels who received Abraham's hospitality. The promise of the Lord is renewed through them: 'Shall I hide from Abraham that which I do: seeing that Abraham shall surely become a great and mighty nation, and all the nations of the earth shall be blessed in him?' It is impossible not to note the connection between circumcision as a symbol of a painfully achieved national unity through the mortification of man, and the promises of future greatness. But this renewal of the promises of the Lord after Abraham's sign of his obedience is a prelude to the judgment of the Lord that Sodom and Gomorrah shall be destroyed. Abraham softens the judgment of the Lord by his pleas, but Sodom and Gomorrah are nevertheless destroyed by fire and brimstone, 'because their sin is very grievous'. Traditionally, the sin of the cities of the plain is sexual licence and perversion. But a special mark of their sin was that they laid hands forcibly upon the angels of the Lord. This is powerful evidence that primitive societies discover unlicensed sex to be a sin not simply against the flesh, but against the spirit. It is seen to threaten the human condition.

The Bible records how the compact marked by circumcision is strengthened as the generations roll on. Moses brings down the tablets of the Law. He fights wrathfully against what we can call foreign practices and ways, and strange gods, and social and religious values alien to the ethos of his own people. We see more clearly in the Scriptural narrative than anywhere else the struggle to weld a people together against all the forces, internal and external, which work to sunder them—against the lures of practices ostensibly religious but in fact evil, against the consequences of conquest, or the economic and spiritual imperialism of stronger peoples, until finally the elaborate laws of Leviticus set a whole people 'within a frame that binds them' and from which it is both anti-social and impious to seek to escape. Leviticus also describes the terrible disaster which can fall upon a people which breaks the will of the Lord. We can read this, at this moment, as a list of the kinds of forces which war against primitive society from its first establishment.

Leviticus 26 speaks of these punishments for those who deny the Lord: 'terror, consumption, and the burning ague, that shall consume the eyes, and cause sorrow of heart: and ye shall sow your seed in vain, for your enemies shall eat it. And I will set my face against you, and ye shall be slain before your enemies: they that hate you shall reign over you; and ye shall flee when none pursueth ... I will make the heaven as iron, and your earth as bars ... your land shall not yield her increase, neither shall the trees of the land yield their fruits.' Plagues, 'wild beasts which shall rob you of your children', diseases to destroy the cattle, and war and captivity are promised, until the cities are laid to waste and 'the sanctuaries are desolate'. The catalogue is not a logical one. But if we consider it as a list of those things which a primitive society had most reason to dread, we must see it also as a list of disasters which a society tried to arm itself to forestall or defeat. They are, firstly, natural disasters such as fire, flood, drought, pestilence, and rapacious wild animals; the help of God may be secured against them; and a tried social solidarity would provide a weapon to endure or defeat them. Next come the hostile acts by other men—war, destruction, captivity, and finally, the loss of the homeland and the laying waste of its hearths and altars.

As we read the Bible, we see that the society so difficult of accomplishment becomes, when established, a matter of pride. The generations are counted back to Abraham, and the pedigrees of the righteous paraded. Proof of descent from the fathers is as much the mark of the covenant as circumcision. Even when we come finally to the life and mission of Christ, his descent from Abraham is recounted as proof of his righteous messiahship. One must not simply belong, one must give *proof* of belonging if called upon. Sir Arthur Grimble in his *Pattern of Islands* gives a charming account of how it was the custom for the islanders when moving through the islands and coming upon new people, to give proof of belonging by reciting as part of their personal introduction their descent from the gods through the known generations; and he himself, in order to be accepted as one of them, had to have invented for him a pedigree which he had to recite as 'proof' of his legitimacy.

The table of ancestry slowly becomes in human affairs of the utmost importance. It is proof of status, rank, tribal or social standing. It is the mark of blood-kinship which cannot be taken from the possessor of it no matter what happens to him. It is only in democratic centuries that it has ceased to be of importance, yet even so, aristocratic claims in our modern world depend on it, kingship rests firmly upon it, and visitors to the Highlands of Scotland would be unwise to assume that it is dead. And we can easily see the rôle it has played in the maintenance of society, a rôle which becomes stronger when the forces of disintegration grow.

All that has been said in this chapter points to the importance of the effort to maintain the tribal identity; it has to be supported by a constant social effort, for it is not natural, not given, but a human artifact. It has to be maintained, first, against nature. Nature is terrible to the man who has escaped it, but stands only just above it. If the opposition of nature is strong enough, the society cannot survive. Then, too, there is the opposition of other peoples—their cultural, economic, military and spiritual aggression. Every strongly united people constitutes a threat of some sort to the peoples surrounding it. By military power or superior techniques or trading capacities it can in one way or another make neighbouring peoples subject to it. But it may do none of these things, and still prove a menace. It may present what I will call spiritual imperialism, and Professor Toynbee calls cultural aggression. One tribe may permit action forbidden in another, or eat foods taboo in another, or worship as friendly gods which others regard as hostile: there is no aggressive intent in these practices—at least, in origin. They simply represent in their totality a different but equally valid pattern of life. The element of cultural aggression enters when one tribe or people discovers that another commits things on which it has set the seal of its disapproval. A conflict may result in which the ways and ideas of one tribe penetrate peacefully the life of another. On the other hand the penetration may be understood as a threat to tribal unity and resisted by war. We who, in the modern world, are accustomed to the conflicts and wars of opposing ideologies ought to find nothing strange in this. If neither war nor cultural penetration results, then we may have the situation in which both parties deliberately seek isolation one from another—an iron curtain in fact. The Australian aborigines who have never resisted the penetration of white man's civilization are dying out from the deep malaise which discouragement has brought. The naked Aucas on the other hand cut off contact with a flight of spears.

Threats to the maintenance of the tribe come from the inside too, from rivalries, jealousies, economic and political competition within the tribe. And so we find that the elaborately structured tribal society gives birth to an immemorial pattern of settling these issues before they can destroy the people. Custom decides all, and the tribal leadership lies with those who have the right to decide wherein, in matters under dispute, the true path of custom lies—with those who have the greatest experience, in fact—the tribal elders. We, when we look back from the heights of civilization, find the rigid patterns and formulae of the past a framework which holds back the mind, which impoverishes the intellectual life of a society, and we disapprove.

But that is only because we are gifted with hind-sight. Were we within such a society, we should see the pattern of rigid tribal custom as the only barrier to the fratricidal anarchy which threatens continually to destroy primitive societies, and which must in its time have led to the extermination of many of them. Among the internal stresses, the greatest must be sex— the jealousies within a tribe for possession of its women. This is such an explosive force within the tribal life that it is subject to powerful controls which hold a delicate balance between restraint and licence, and circumcision is a universal symbol of this balance.

Sexual discipline cannot begin until incest is abolished. The dominant male, the father of a group, has by the mere fact of his control over the household gathered under his roof or within his shelter and protection, access to all the women, young, old, or merely children, related or not, living with him. Were that power of access used to gratify his sexual appetites, then there would be no hope of establishing any tribal, that is to say, social, sexual discipline. *Quis custodiet ipsos custodes?* But such power of access downwards, so to speak, from the father, would rouse up eventually in its train, by mere example, incest *upwards*, by the young males, through sisters and lubras to the mother. Incest is capable of generating a force so explosive as to annihilate the family in murder and lust, and prevent any approach at all to social or tribal stability. It is therefore necessary to speak of the dread of incest next.

CHAPTER 5

The Supreme Taboo

There is a remarkable passage in the third book of David Hume's *A Treatise of Human Nature* in which the distinction between the animal and the human attitudes to incest is discussed in order to show that moral feelings are of subjective origin. 'I would fain ask any one, why Incest in the human species is criminal, and why the very same action, and in the same relations in animals, have not the smallest moral turpitude and deformity? If it be answered, that this action is innocent in animals, because they have not reason sufficient to discover its turpitude; but that man, being endowed with that faculty, which *ought* to restrain him to his duty, the same action instantly becomes criminal to him. Should this be said, I would reply, that this is evidently arguing in a circle. For, before reason can perceive this turpitude, the turpitude must exist; and consequently is independent of the decisions of our reason, and is their object more properly than their effect. According to this system, then, every animal that has sense and appetite and will, that is, every animal must be susceptible of all the same virtues and vices, for which we ascribe praise and blame to human creatures. . . . Their want of a sufficient degree of reason may hinder them from perceiving the duties and obligations of morality, but can never hinder these duties from existing.'[1] But this was self-evidently the wrong way to discover the nature of morality, he argued. Morality did not consist in any relations

[1] Op. cit., Bk. III, Pt. 1, Sec. I.

which could be exposed by science. It did not even consist in any matters of fact which could be discovered by the understanding. It was not an object of reason but, like beauty, was in the eye of the beholder. 'Vice and virtue, therefore may be compared to sounds, colours, heat, and cold, which according to modern philosophy, are not qualities in objects but perceptions in the mind.'[1]

It is therefore within himself that man *feels* that this act is right and that is wrong. Where does this feeling come from, if it is not a product of the external constellation of things? Is it a gift from Nature? Nature is an ambiguous word, and much depends on how we define it. Hume prefers to conclude that our feelings about what is right and wrong derive from the usefulness to us of this or that arrangement. 'Virtue is distinguished by the pleasure, and vice by the pain, that any action, sentiment, or character, gives us by the mere view and contemplation'—a pronouncement that Jeremy Bentham was to exploit very successfully. 'This decision is very commodious,' Hume remarked. Unfortunately, he did not find the decision commodious enough. Hume was not a philosopher given to self-deception, and the more he pursued the 'pleasure-pain-principle' of morality, the more it gave him to pause. For, as he wrote, 'it is certain that self-love, when it acts at its liberty, instead of engaging us to honest actions, is the source of all injustice and violence; nor can a man ever correct those vices without correcting and restraining the *natural* movements of that appetite.'[2] And so he was forced back on to the notion of morality as the result of a mutual contract among men to respect each other's goods and persons.

This is not the place to pursue the moral ideas of so important a philosopher, which in any case I have done elsewhere,[3] but his rejection of a purely natural source of morality, a doctrine which attracted his contemporary, Jean-Jacques Rousseau, is of course relevant to the theme of this book. What then of his

[1] Ibid.
[2] Ibid., Bk. III, Pt. 1, Sec. III.
[3] Cf. *The English Philosophers*, London, 1953, pp. 153 et seq.

argument of the subjectivity of moral values? This is a barren line of speculation unless one asks why men should have this moral capacity, or even subjectivity itself, while animals have it not. And if, in pursuit of this, one reaches the conclusion that men have it because they see that certain courses are harmful to their relations to their fellows, while to animals such dilemmas do not exist, one is only really saying that the human nexus contains elements, patterns, relationships of which the animal world is not capable: relations of morality being among them. What accounts for this situation?

It is singularly useless therefore to invoke the relativity of moral values from culture to culture. What is more important is to establish why there should be a moral realm at all about which it is possible for judgments to be relative (if in fact they always are). I think it can be shown that though man reaches from time to time different decisions about his moral duties, the same moral sphere presses upon all men. Men's answers to its demands will not always be the same: even the same man in one life-time will make many different decisions as to where his moral duty lies. And sometimes he will make decisions which are self-deceiving or hypocritical—decisions which will allow him what he knows is forbidden, or will enable him to enjoy secretly that which he has publicly renounced. Not only the fallibility of man but his corruption is evident here, and it is this which must make us wary of accepting too easily arguments about the relativity of morals. The pressure of the moral sphere nevertheless remains.

If we remember that our task is to see in what ways man has escaped from nature into another sphere, we cannot do better than to look at what must be man's first response to the revelation of the moral sphere in which he must live. I mean the incest taboo, which appears to be a universal one, and therefore in a sense is man's first moral absolute. Of course, it is said even of incest that primitive man's horror is not our horror, and this is sometimes put in such a way as to suggest that the views of antiquity were pathological, and that in any case there were people who were not affected by it. The Pharaohs are invariably cited, and about the practices of ancient royal kings, Sir James Frazer had this to say:

'Among the stories which were told of Cinyras, the ancestor of the priestly kings of Paphos and the father of Adonis, there are some that deserve our attention. In the first place, he is said to have begotten his son Adonis in incestuous intercourse with his daughter Myrrha at a festival of the corn-goddess, at which women in white were wont to offer corn-wreaths as first-fruits of the harvest and to observe strict chastity for nine days. Similar cases of incest with a daughter are reported of many ancient kings. It seems unlikely that such reports are without foundation, and perhaps equally improbable that they refer to a mere fortuitous outburst of natural lust. We may suspect that they are based on a practice actually observed for a definite reason in certain special circumstances. Now in countries where the royal blood was traced through women only, and where consequently the king held office merely in virtue of his marriage with an hereditary princess, who was the real sovereign, it appears to have often happened that a prince would marry his own sister, the princess royal, in order to obtain with her hand the crown which otherwise would have gone to another man, perhaps to a stranger. May not the same rule of descent have furnished a motive for incest with a daughter? For it seems a natural corollary from such a rule that the king was bound to vacate the throne on the death of his wife, the queen, since he occupied it only by virtue of his marriage with her. When that marriage terminated, his right to the throne terminated with it and passed at once to his daughter's husband. Hence if the king desired to reign after his wife's death, the only way in which he could legitimately continue to do so was by marrying his daughter, and thus prolonging through her the title which had formerly been his through her mother.'[1]

We do not know how such actions were received in their day, but exceptional reasons of state do not constitute an overthrow of accepted morality. One hesitates to imagine what Henry VIII would have done to one of his subjects who treated his own

---

[1] *The Golden Bough*, Abridged Edn., 1949, p. 332.

lawful wife as his king had treated a succession of wives. Human sacrifice, as a solemn religious theme, is the subject of the whole of *The Golden Bough*, but no one imagines that in societies where ritual human sacrifice was periodically performed, non-sacred murder was equally honoured as within the law. It has been accepted since time immemorial that priests and kings—and still more, priest-kings—by virtue of their offices and powers, were under the awful necessity of doing deeds which would have brought disaster and divine retribution to ordinary mortals, but from the consequences of which they were saved by their sacredness, their divinity or semi-divinity. This indeed constitutes one source of the awe in which they were held. But that the gods did it would not have been an acceptable plea in a Greek court of law for exalted citizens, let alone ordinary ones.

In fact, sacred exceptions apart, it is difficult not to conclude that dread of incest is universal. The argument about relativity of morals in the case of incest falls to the ground. To speak of subjectivity means nothing. For of course it is in his inwardness, in his spirit, that man comes to his moral conclusions. But there is no reason to suppose that the gods do not speak to him there; nor is there any reason to imagine that what he concludes there is not properly derived from a study of the external constellation of things. No matter to what primitive people one turns, incest meets with horrified condemnation and is held to merit exile or death. It provokes an emotional shock far greater than that aroused by murder. And in people after people we find that the most elaborate social institutions have come into being to render *accidental* incest impossible, and *intentional* incest so manifest and culpable that it can be detected and punished with the greatest of ease. Clans and sub-clans, totemic groups and marriage groups, and similar social institutions enforcing exogamy are almost universal. Of these I shall have something to say. But social institutions mark firmly and publicly the groups tabooed to each other and do so with a force greater than any law as we understand it in the west. Even so, they are seldom regarded as sufficient to overcome incestuous desires. They are invariably discovered side by side with a most rigid etiquette which cuts the contacts between brothers and sisters to a minimum, and ensures that such a minimum is conducted in the public view: thus Margaret Mead, in *Coming of Age in Samoa*, writes:

'The most important relationships within a Samoan household which influence the lives of the young people are the relationships between the boys and girls who call each other "brother" and "sister", whether by blood, marriage or adoption, and the relationship between younger and older relatives. The stress upon the sex difference between contemporaries and the emphasis on relative age are amply explained by the conditions of family life. Relatives of opposite sex have a most rigid code of etiquette prescribed for all their contacts with each other. After they have reached years of discretion—nine or ten years of age in this case—they may not touch each other, sit close together, eat together, address each other familiarly, or mention any salacious matter in each other's presence. They may not remain in any house, except their own, together, unless half the village is gathered there. They may not walk together, use each other's possessions, dance on the same floor, or take part in any of the same small group activities. This strict avoidance applies to all individuals of the opposite sex within five years above or below one's own age with whom one was reared or to whom one acknowledges any relationship by blood or marriage. The conformance to this brother and sister taboo begins when the younger of the two children feels "ashamed" at the elder's touch and continues until old age when the decrepit, toothless pair of old siblings may again sit on the same mat and not feel ashamed.'[1]

And later she speaks of deviations from the normal pattern of sex relations and explains that among the worst of these is any case where an older man falls in love with some young and dependent woman or girl of his household, his adopted child or wife's younger sister for example. 'The cry of incest is raised against him, and sometimes feeling runs so high that he has to leave the group.'[2]

Malinowski, in that classic investigation, *The Sexual Life of*

[1] Op. cit., London, 1929, pp. 43-4.   [2] Ibid., p. 89.

Savages, tells much the same story about the Trobrianders, those attractive pagans whose life he watched with such minute and loving care. When a Trobriand boy grows up, and there is a sister of his living in the house, he has to go and sleep in the Bachelors' house. It is not really a house reserved exclusively to youths, as may occur in some primitive societies, but a place where young men carry on undisturbed their liaisons with the concubines they take before marriage. So the dispatch of the youth to the bachelors' quarters has nothing to do with the preservation of sexual morality in general, but simply with the etiquette that forbids him to live under the same roof as his sister. In her love affairs the sister must at all costs avoid being seen by her brother: Malinowski was told that if by chance a man came upon his sister while she was making love to her sweetheart, all three would have to commit suicide by jumping from a coconut palm according to the traditional manner of public atonement, called *lo'u*. 'When, on certain occasions, brother and sister have to appear in the same company—when they travel in the same canoe, for instance, or participate in a domestic meeting—a rigidity of behaviour and a sobriety of conversation fall upon all those present. No cheerful company, no festive entertainment, therefore, is allowed to include brother and sister, since their simultaneous presence would throw a blight on pleasure and would chill gaiety.'[1]

If incest among the Trobrianders is discovered, then there is no full social remedy but suicide. Even the public (but unproved) accusation of incest is so mortal a blow to a person's pride, that suicide follows as a matter of course. 'What would happen,' Malinowski asked, 'if incest were not discovered?' The answer is that it produces a painful and probably fatal disease. The belly swells, the skin becomes white and breaks out into sores, and the victim 'fades away in a wasting sickness'.

In his table of relationship terms, Malinowski gives 'Luguta' as the term a man applies to his sister, or a woman to her brother; but it is also applied by a man to a woman of the same clan and generation, and by a woman to a man of the same

[1] *The Sexual Life of Savages*, London, 1932, pp. 438-9.

clan and generation, that is to say to all of one generation who are taboo to each other. The sexual taboo has wider application of course than simply to the persons officially designated as 'luguta' (sister): it stretches to the parent and one's own children of the opposite sex. The term is in fact applied to all tabooed relationships. This is an extremely good example of the value of a social institution in the prevention even of accidental incest. By the rejection of *any* endogamous sexual relationship—any relationship at all with a member of one's own clan—long absence, the death of parents, the uprooting of homes, which might produce the cessation of contact or the loss of knowledge of kinship relations, or any other accidents which might open the door to incest, are avoided. A Trobriand Oedipus could never have married his mother Jocasta, no matter how separated by time and place their lives had been lived, while they both remembered their clan designation. And whatever else happens the contracting parties are unlikely to forget that. And these elaborate social precautions are taken in a primitive society whose members do not associate sexual intercourse with child-bearing! It suggests to me either turning the blind eye, or a profound if unconscious understanding of what is involved in sex—that its explosive power in society would hardly be less even if it had no direct relationship to the birth of children. When a man and woman cleave together and become as one flesh that is an alteration of status in the eyes of all aware of it.

Malinowski narrates a tragic myth of incest which he believes to lie near the heart of the Trobrianders and to govern their sexual life. It concerns two beautiful children, a boy and a girl, brother and sister. The boy had collected magical herbs and cooked them in coconut oil to make a love potion. He hung the vessel containing the love fluid from the roof near the door of the family hut. There he left it and went away to bathe in the lagoon. His sister returned from gathering firewood and presently entered the hut. Her head brushed against the bottle containing the magic potion, it trickled into her hair, she passed her hands over her head and wiped off the oil and smelt it, and the magic entered into her. Trembling, she asked where her brother had gone, and her mother said, 'O my children, they have become mad! He has gone to the open seashore.' The girl ran towards the open sea. When she came to the beach, she untied her fibre skirt and flung it down. She sped naked along the beach, seeking her brother, and found him bathing. She entered the water and gave chase to him, up and down the lagoon, and finally she caught him and they lay down together in the sea and had intercourse with each other. Overcome with passion, they went together to the grotto on the seashore, a local landmark, and there lay together again and again, and did not eat or drink, for they were filled with shame, and so they died, unparted. A fisherman of Iwa had a dream that same night. He dreamt of the mint plant which is used in love potions and that two people, brother and sister, were together through its power in the island grotto. He went out that day and searched for them and as he climbed the slope towards the grotto a frigate bird rose, as though it had caught the scent of humans. This incident led him towards them and soon he caught sight of the prostrate figures and lo! a mint flower had sprouted through their breasts.

It is a story of the flame and the sadness of consuming desire and perhaps Malinowski is right when he says that it witnesses not only to the curse placed upon incest, but to the fact that it gets defied, and that the story may even be one means of inspiring the adventurous young to break it. However, the story no more breathes such intention than *Oedipus Rex*, though it is unmistakably full of pity and compassion. It understands the tragedy, but it makes no effort to minimize it.

As the Trobrianders tell the story, the myth might have been an event of the day before yesterday, but it is difficult to conceive of the telling of a myth with such a contemporary flavour among the Murngin peoples who live in the most northern tip of Australia by the Torres Strait and the Gulf of Carpentaria. Professor W. Lloyd Warner told their story in *A Black Civilization: A Social Study of an Australian Tribe*.[1] They have plenty of

[1] London, 1937.

incestuous stories, but they are all related as if they belonged to the distant past, and I do not recollect a brother and sister story among them. Among the Murngin, the brother and sister relationship is surrounded by taboos as strict as may be found elsewhere. If a brother speaks in the hearing of a sister, he speaks in a low voice, for she is not supposed to hear him. She must use the same discretion. He will not even talk directly to her, nor she to him, nor will he use before her the obscenities which are permitted before all other women including his mother. By a strict etiquette, he must not allow others to do or say in his presence what is not permitted to him. Professor Warner says: 'Ordinarily, when a man's anger rises [among the Murngins], he immediately bursts into an almost pyrotechnical display of abuse, most of it centering around sex, breaking of incest taboos, peculiarities of the genitalia, irregularities in the sexual act between men and women, et cetera. The aversion to hearing or using such profanity in front of a sister is called "mirrirri" (earthing). It really means, "My ear can't hear obscenity in front of my sister". An older man said, "It is just the same as if I had been hit on the head with a club when I hear that." Another said, "My heart jumps and stops, jumps and stops, when I hear that mirrirri," '[1] and the author tells the story of how a youth heard his sister being abused with sexual language by her husband. He threw spears at his sister and at all the women of the camp who stood in moiety sister relationship with him. This apparently odd ritual is consistent. The offended brother will throw spears at the sister and similarly related women, rather than at the men, for this registers his protest without starting the general fight which would be bound to occur if he threw the spears at the offending men.

A brother and sister never sleep in the same hut, except as infants, nor are they supposed to touch each other. At the early age of six or eight the little boy is taken away and circumcised and then he leaves his family hut or place and goes to the boys' camp, and lives among boys of his own age, presided over by an older man. This does not mean that the boy loses contact with

[1] *A Black Civilisation*, p. 66.

his family, only that he does not sleep with them. The Murngins believe that from about the age of circumcision the boy is capable of noticing the sexual relations of the adults of his home. Even though these relations, in the almost total lack of common privacy which is general in tribes who lack proper dwelling-places, are conducted with the utmost discretion, yet the Murngins say, 'It is all right for children to watch, for they don't know what is happening, but when a boy gets older he sees, and then he says, "That's good for me, too." He goes and gets a young girl, maybe a galle (potential future wife) to him, and they go into the bush.'[1] Or 'When he stays in the big camp, he sees too many women'—and does not learn how to behave properly as a man. Among these naked people there is a deep sense of shame over many such things. For instance: 'After his first intercourse with his wife following the birth of a child, the husband always rises early and bathes himself. If he did not, he would look like an animal to the other men and feel ashamed before them.'[2] After a boy has been circumcised, he is told, 'You must not use obscene language. You must never tell a lie. You must not commit adultery, nor go after women who do not belong to you. You must always obey your father and respect your elders. You must never betray the secrets that you have learned from us to the women or the boys who have not been circumcised.'[3]

Within the tribes, incest is controlled by the 'moieties' into which they are divided. There are two, Dua and Yiritja, and sexual intercourse is not allowed between members of the same moiety. How rigidly this is enforced by etiquette as well as law Professor Warner illustrates from one of the autobiographies told to him. The black fellow said to him that, as a very small child, no more than three or four years old, he had played with other boys and girls of the tribe at 'keeping house' or 'mothers and fathers', even though he and they did not know all that this meant. Nevertheless the two sexes called each other by the right terms, and held to the accepted categories. ' "No Yiritja boy ever played house with a Yiritja girl and no Dua boy ever

[1] Ibid., p. 127.   [2] Ibid., p. 78.   [3] Ibid., p. 288.

id this with a Dua girl. We always did this properly." On
eing asked how they, as children, knew this was the right way,
e said, "That is something I always knew." [1]

The Murngin people relate, and re-enact in their endless and
omplicated ceremonies, what can only be described as a
Creation Myth. It concerns the two Wawilak Women who
walked from the southern interior of Australia to the northern
ands and founded the Murngin people. This happened in the
days when everything was different, when animals were men,
and when the totemic spirits from the underground walked
about like modern men, and men properly so-called had not
appeared. One of the Wawilak women was pregnant, and the
other carried a baby under her arm in a bark cradle. It was a
boy. The two sisters, who had no men with them, talked
various languages as they passed through various lands, and
named the places they saw, and rested at, and this gave the
lands the languages they now enjoyed. But in the Wawilak
country they committed an irreparable act—they had intercourse with Wawilak Wongar (totemic spirit) men. But these
men were Dua, and the women were Dua, and the act was
unforgivably against the whole tribal spirit.

The child of the younger woman was born, and the two
sisters continued their pilgrimage, naming all the clan terri-
tories of the Dua moiety. They did not stop until they reached
the Mirrirmina water hole in the country of the Liaalaomir clan.
At the bottom of this water hole dwelt Yurlunggur, the great
copper snake or python, who was the totem of the Dua clan. The
sisters named this country too, and with a fire drill the older
sister made a fire and started cooking all the food that had been
gathered on the journey. But no sooner did they start to cook an
animal or plant than it jumped out of the fire and ran to the
Mirrirmina water hole and jumped in.

Now a second folly occurred. All unbeknown to herself the
menstrual blood of the elder woman fouled the waters of the
totem well where the great python lived: this happened when
the elder woman was gathering paper bark to make a bed for

[1] Ibid., p. 32.

her sister's new-born baby. The python smelt the pollution and stirred in his well. He crawled out and spat some of the well water into the sky where it formed a cloud from which the rain fell. But as Yurlunggur rose out of the well the water rose with him and it flooded the earth. Yurlunggur saw the women and their babies. He hissed down upon them more rain. They built themselves a shelter and hid in it from the rain, for they did not know that it was the consequence of the defilement of the totem well. Indeed, the women sang the sacred totemic songs in the hope that they would stop the rain. They sang stronger and stronger songs as the rain grew stronger and stronger. But the rain did not stop and Yurlunggur swallowed the women and their children, and the earth was covered with flood, to the height that he towered above it.

The totemic snakes and the great python met and discussed what they had been eating. All the snakes confessed except Yurlunggur, who was most reluctant to admit what he had done. But he was persuaded, almost forced, and confessed that he had eaten the two women and their two children. The moment he said this, the south-eastern monsoon began to blow and Yurlunggur fell to the ground, and his weight split it. He spewed up the women and children. One of the totemic snakes was disgusted—you've eaten your own brothers and sisters, it alleged. The women and their two children came to life again, but the python swallowed them again. He swam underground to the Wawilak country and there spat out the women for the last time, and they became blocks of stone which can be seen standing there at the present time. But the boys, Yurlunggur kept inside him.

At the moment when the two women had been swallowed by the serpent they had been preparing to circumcise their sons. But they had been given no time to do so; but because they wanted to do so, and proposed that other people should do so too, people respect their wishes, and cut their sons today.

Men were initiated into the secrets of the creative deeds of the sisters, and of their death and destruction at the hands of the python, because their inquisitive ancestors had followed in the tracks of the women and listened to all that went on. Of course, these ancestors were not *modern* men, but Wongar (totemic) men. Finally, all that the sisters had done was revealed to the totemic men in a dream and they learnt the songs and dances they were commanded to transmit to the tribe. 'The two sisters said to the men, "This [the dream instruction] is all now. We are giving you this dream so you can remember these important things. You must never forget these things we have told you tonight. You must remember every time each year these songs and dances. You must paint with blood and feathers. . . You must dance all the things we saw and named on our journey and which ran away into the well." '[1] And the men danced the dances and ceremonies as soon as they got back into their own country and to-day men say 'We dance these things now, because our Wongar ancestors learned them from the two Wawilak sisters'.

The Murngin people (who live, incidentally, in a climate of disastrous extremes of flood and drought) interpret this legend as a fall both of man *and of nature* principally through the incestuous acts of the two sisters. The cycle of creation, the seasons with the growth and decay of vegetation, copulation, birth and death of animals as well as man, are all the fault of those two Wawilak sisters.

'If they hadn't done wrong in their own country and copulated with Dua Wongar men [an incestuous act] and then come down to the Liaalaomir country and menstruated and made that snake wild . . .' the natural disasters would never have occurred. 'Everyone and all the plants and animals would have walked about by themselves.' There would have been no copulation between the sexes and no children and no change. 'After they had done this wrong they [the sisters] made it the law for everyone'[2]—that man should sin! In fact, sin, death, decay and corruption enter into the world with incest and sexual defilement: or to put it more accurately, the menstrual flow can defile a particular place, but incest is a defilement of the universe, bound to produce a violent reaction which alters the constella-

[1] Ibid., p. 259.   [2] Ibid., p. 385.

tion of things unfavourably to man. It calls down that which the Priest of Zeus laments to Oedipus:

'The city, as thou thyself seest, is now too sorely vexed, and can no more lift her head from beneath the angry waves of death; a blight is on her in the fruitful blossoms of the land, in the herds among the pastures, in the barren pangs of women, and withal the flaming god, the malign plague, hath swooped on us, and ravages the town; by whom the house of Cadmus is made waste, but dark hades rich in groans and tears.'

The Balinese are in no sense a primitive people. They enjoy a sophisticated and exquisite civilization. Yet with them horror of incest extends even to babes in the womb.

'Whenever twins are born, say two boys or two girls, "misfortune befalls" the family. But should a boy and girl be born, it spells disaster for the whole village. When the children came into the world the *kulkul* sounded the alarm all through the night, and in the morning the village was declared *sebel*, or impure. The temple closed its doors and for a whole year no one will be allowed to enter it. The whole life of the village will be paralysed. The "guilty" parents were expelled from the *desa* and the babies taken to the graveyard, where according to custom the father and mother went to rescue them. The house in which the twins were born was pulled down and burned. Parents and twins will only be allowed back into the village forty-two days after the birth, and this only should they have the means to pay the expenses of the *mejaru*, or purification ceremony . . . [which are very high indeed]. . . In the minds of the simple people of the island, a brother and sister, who are twins, and thus united in their mother's womb, are believed to commit a kind of incest, a crime punishable with death.'[1]

It is not necessary to continue to multiply examples, fascinating though the theme may be. The important imaginative act is to understand the horror of incest, not simply as we feel it in our own post-Freudian souls, but as it may have looked in the first dawn. Freud made a remarkable effort in *Totem and Tabu*. There, basing himself upon Darwin's notion of the primal

[1] *Bliss in Bali* by Jacques Chegaray, London, 1955, p. 86.

horde as the first human society, he adduced a rivalry between the young males and the Old Man (the archetypal father) for the possession of the women of the family. This rivalry resulted in the expulsion of the young males from the horde, an event often to be witnessed in the animal herd. 'One day the expelled brothers joined forces, slew and ate the father, and thus put an end to the father horde. Together they dared and accomplished what would have remained impossible for them singly. Perhaps some advance in culture, like the use of a new weapon, had given them the feeling of superiority. Of course these cannibalistic savages ate their victim. This violent primal father had surely been the envied and feared model for each of the brothers. Now they accomplished their identification with him by devouring him and each acquired a part of his strength. The totem feast, which is perhaps mankind's first celebration, would be the repetition and commemoration of this memorable, criminal act with which so many things began, social organization, moral restrictions and religion.'[1]

This lawless deed was, in fact, the beginning of the law! The feelings of the sons towards the father were not wholly hostile: they admired and loved him too. Having killed and eaten the father, remorse and guilt and pity arose in them and produced that state of repentance and shame which prohibited them from taking over the living loot their deed had won them. They must, instead, go on to institute the social compact which, in the form of totemism, banned forever incestuous unions. One deed of horror gave birth to the realization of the horror of the other deed.

Of course, Freud is inventing a myth to justify his own psychological investigations into the hostility of the young for their parents. Having discovered at the same time traces of in-fantile totemism, he decided to link up the two themes in one great historical exposition. In fact, he is speculating about the *origins* of structured human society, of which we know almost nothing. His own speculation however has shifted the emphasis away from incest to murder. It is the murder which occurs, and

---

[1] *Totem and Tabu*, London, 1919, pp. 235-6.

not the incestuous act. And it is the more remarkable that this is so because, as he himself writes, the primitive savage is not the neurotic. The neurotic takes the thought for the deed. The savage proceeds straight to the deed. Yet in the Freudian myth the savage is made to behave like a neurotic, and to shrink from the deed he has planned because of an attack of remorse after the success of his first undertaking. Yet, if having killed the Old Man, and become heirs to his estate, the young males do not go on to incest, but draw back from it, one can only say that they must have been possessed of enough sensitivity of conscience not to embark on father-murder in the first place either. And if, too, they had been possessed of enough political sagacity to act as a united team before and after the murder, and to remain united, even in withdrawal from their original plan, and able to impose an elaborate social form on the society they had inherited—then they must have been equipped with sufficient foresight to see how abominable and impossible the plan was to begin with. If it is accepted however that the band of brothers got rid of the father in the way which Freud describes, but then shrank from incest, I think we can say that what made them shrink was not remorse or pity at murder and cannibalism, but horror of incest itself as a crime of the first magnitude, in its own right, and independent of any other guilty associations. We must accept however that the slaughter of the Old Man could deepen the sense of horror which surrounds incest, by revealing some of its consequences in family and social life.

Yet Freud's argument depends upon the assumption that the Oedipus situation came first, historically speaking. There is nothing to prove that it did. On the contrary, it looks as though the primary struggle of mankind (if we can even speak of such a thing) was not against the father, but against the mother. And even then, not against the mother in the sense in which civilized man reads back into the primitive his own tensions, his Oedipean jealousies, but rather of the struggle over the problems which arise from the increasing independence of Maternity which must face every child as it grows. The relation of mother and child is tender, relaxed, uncritical, warm. There is a reluc-

tance on the part of the child to leave the paradise of lap and
breast, and on the part of the mother to lose the dependent
babe. Yet just as the child left its mother's body to be born, so
too it must finally abandon the mother's breast and become
physically independent, and its own physical growth and the
arrival of other children will push it along this road, even
though mother and child both seek to delay the inevitable. The
growth of the child's consciousness is correlated with the
physical changes: psychical maturity means that the spiritual
and intellectual development has moved in harmony with this
very real physical emancipation. The process means that valuable spiritual bonds must be broken. If one accepts that the
pattern of childhood provides clues to the childhood of the
human race (a somewhat dangerous analogy) then it is possible
to argue that the half-unwilling struggle of the child to free itself from dependence on the mother and to achieve self-
realization through freedom and independence is the prototype
of the most primitive human situation: in this way, through the
pain, loneliness and alarmingness of separation, man came to
self-consciousness. Certainly this is so for Erich Neumann, who
argues out the point in elaborate Jungian terms in *The Origins
and History of Consciousness*. The matriarchal supremacy takes
historical precedence for him over the patriarchal situation which
Freud exploits. There could be no Oedipus situation, in
which the son was the rival for the mother's love, and revolted
against the tyrannical sexual monopoly of the father, unless the
father really was the dominant male who had freed himself
from physical and psychological dependence on womenkind, on
'the universal tribal mother', and subjected women to his convenience in turn, nor unless the son was able to conceive of himself as a separate self with appetitive rights of his own. Where
both father and son were under matriarchal subjection, rivalry
between them was less likely than the mutual discovery of their
maleness, and the forming of an alliance between them to
oppose the female domination: the Oedipus situation was in
fact impossible where father and son were both children of the
Great Mother, and ineffectively masculine. One may conclude

that the birth of human society and the discovery of incest go back before the time that the old-gorilla-male dominated the band, if ever such a time existed. We cannot therefore base the abhorrence of incest upon the social rationalization and resolution of the Oedipus situation.

Psychological explanations of all this are in any case suspect. They must necessarily deal with the human givenness, and analyse it to reveal its contents. But what is the source of the human givenness? A. N. Whitehead argued in *Process and Reality* and elsewhere that rationality could be made to account for everything except the ground for rationality. In the same way it can be said that psychology can handle almost everything in the human psyche except the fact that there is a human psyche to handle. It is conceivable, and indeed I would argue it, that morality is part of the human givenness and that even Oedipus theories deal not with the origin of morality, but with the post-moral situation. It is probable that the recoil from incest is the mark of the gift of morality, and this itself is the revelation which comes when man moves from nature into the dimension of the spiritual. It is the first morality, which creates human prohibitions, and without prohibitions there are no psychological tensions, certainly not the kind which result in a tug-of-war of opposed impulses within the soul, and therefore we must say, no psyche, as the psychologists of most schools would conceive it. It is then impossible to look for an explanation of the dread of incest purely in psychological terms.

In a purely rational ethic, one might think that murder ought to be more bitterly condemned than incest, for murder extinguishes a life which cannot be replaced or renewed, and to the savage all death is murder, to be avenged if possible. The murderer is part of the dark forces working against the living, and rightly to be dreaded and destroyed. One can only assert that though, possibly, rationally, this ought to be so, it is *not* so in the psychology of primitive peoples. Murder is one of the two basic crimes condemned by primitive peoples, it is true, but there is a sense in which murder is more normal, is more easily comprehended and condoned than incest, no matter how clearly it may be formally condemned. Incest and sexual crime are the irreparable 'spoilers of the land', whereas for murder accepted scales of reparation may be drawn up, including guilt-money. But it is not always formally condemned except as between members of the tribe itself. Murder parties in many tribes are openly and honourably formed: among the aborigines, a vengeance party may be gathered with all ceremony, proceed to its killing, and if successful be received back into the tribe with ritual raptures. The murdered one is feared both for the revenge his spirit may take, and for the feud which may be provoked with his relatives. But this does not deter the aborigines, or most primitive peoples: magical ceremonies and ritual purifications are supposed to take care of that.

Among many primitive peoples no brave is finally acceptable until he has killed a man and blooded his spear or sword; and the rôles of head-hunting, or scalp-hunting and feuding are so well known that they need only to be mentioned to show beyond any doubt that what is justly called murder is regarded as a means of glory. So that we can speak of degrees of killing, from the condemned murder of a kinsman, to the killing in sport or combat which brings a glow to the heart of a savage. On the other hand, there are no 'degrees' of incest.

Finally, we find ourselves moving into that dark terrain where murder and cannibalism meet, where, as in parts of Liberia in the past, there was a trade in human flesh, and a business of murder. Not only has murder not been so universally condemned as incest, but the eating of human flesh either ritually or out of hunger has not been universally condemned either, and has only in the last century begun to die out among primitive peoples as a result of civilized pressures. It is the Wawilak women who were condemned for incest, not the Python for cannibalism. Murder, though recognized as a crime crying out for vengeance, does not carry the moral stigma of incest, even though incest extinguishes no life, and may even produce new life. There are no elaborate social institutions to make certain the avoidance of murder as there are those to produce the avoidance of incest. Incest, and not murder or cannibalism, is the fundamental human crime.

If this is so, then we meet in it the fundamental moral aversion, the fundamental moral decision of humanity. The wrong less immediately obvious to primitive minds (especially, one might imagine, to those who do not associate intercourse with child-bearing) is nevertheless in those minds particularly the worst sin which a man can commit. It is therefore extremely necessary to ask—*why?*

Here, neither the creation of a new myth, nor the invention of a new anthropology is asked of us, but a task of the imagination. Murder destroys a man, but the society remains. Society imposes a penalty, some satisfaction is made, and the authority of society rests unchallenged still. Incest destroys a society, corrupting it from within, in the very heart of the family unit upon which society rests and from which it springs; or makes it impossible, despite men's longings, for that society ever to rise up, and condemns men to that state, of which Thomas Hobbes spoke, in which there is 'no society; and which is worst of all; continual fear, and danger of violent death; and the life of man, solitary, poor, nasty, brutish, and short'. Incest is the sin against all.

Yet that is no final answer. To the animal there is nothing reprehensible; to man incest is entirely reprehensible; and here, in a sense, is the great divide. The most damaging form of incest—socially speaking—is brother-sister incest, since this can lead to a lifelong union basing itself upon a fundamental family corruption which can be endlessly repeated from the incestuous parents downwards—parental incest leading to incest with the offspring, and incest among the offspring. Primitive societies recognize this, and recognize also that it is not enough for the union of brother and sister to be made impossible by law (that is by exogamic institutions), it has to be made psychologically impossible by an unnatural separation between brother and sister at those stages in life when such unions might be formed in innocence of the law. Hence the rigid tribal etiquette forbidding any sort of intimacy between the tiniest of brothers and sisters, and making the brother the punctilious guardian of morals and modesty when the sister is present. This etiquette is a means of

compelling the child to learn the meaning of incest, and Malinowski has a revealing passage where he speaks of the fact that
the Trobriand child is not normally punished or severely
scolded, and so it 'receives a real shock when suddenly it is
roughly handled, seriously reprimanded or punished whenever
it makes any friendly, affectionate, or even playful advances to
the other small being constantly about in the same household.
Above all, the child experiences an emotional shock when it
becomes aware of the expression of horror and anguish on the
faces of its elders when they correct it.'[1] Malinoswki describes
the process as an 'emotional contagion', born of the perception
of the moral reactions of others. The mere fact that each generation must learn in turn to come out of its innocence to knowledge
of forbidden fruit is precisely what endows brother-sister incest
in childhood or early youth with tragedy: in the Trobriand
myth the boy and the girl are doomed creatures, half innocent,
half aware, caught by fate. But though more tragic, the brother-
sister incest is less culpable than the incest directed downwards,
from father to daughter, from mother to son. And against this
no etiquette or formality can ever provide, for nothing can and
nothing ought to separate parents and children psychologically
or physically, since the loss of the love of one for the other would
be fatal for humanity.

Of necessity, the offspring of all creatures enjoy a special
relationship of dependence, tenderness and confidence, certainly to the female, often to the male parent too. This mutual
trust and love into which no law can successfully intrude and
which no etiquette can organize is magnificently heightened in
human relations, and so completely realized that the family
relationship created by a birth is one which is destined to
endure, accidents apart, for the lifetimes both of the children
and of the parents. The children will always be the children
of such and such parents, no matter how old they grow, or
how long they outlive their parents. The relationship is never
extinguished, either by maturity or by death. Nor can the
parents, however long they live, and are of whole mind, ever

[1] *The Sexual Life of Savages*, p. 438.

grow unaware that these their children are these their children. The relationship remains even when all that belongs to it during childhood is fallen away and forgotten. It is not simply that this is the case from external observation, so to speak, but that both parents know it in their blood: it is part of the human givenness: they know it as a normal fact of existence which gives content to such words as 'mother', 'father', 'daughter', 'son'. They know what it involves through the imaginative power to reconstruct in their own minds the conscious processes of other lives than their own. They know what their children have been through, and must go through as they grow up, they know long before the children do, no matter how primitive the society, what is in store for them in the awakening of sex, in the power it will exert on them, in the fascinations with which it will lure them, in the economic and social responsibilities it will exact from them. They know these things looking forward to a time which is not yet, and by looking back to the past, to a distant childhood. They make comparisons. I do not say that they know these things as I perhaps can write them down, as rational chains of argument or description, but as things deeply, intuitively felt and remembered, charged with emotion, and the subtle awakening of the intellect that emotion brings. They remember emotionally the relation of trust, and even the sense of awe before their own parents. They know from experience what the difference is between a passing lust and a married partnership.

The *primary* incestuous opportunity, the first temptation, is that which is presented to parents by the accessibility of their own young. And against this no possible social institution can erect a barrier. The barriers erected therefore are nearly all directed against brother-sister incest. And this is to say just what the horror on the faces of Trobriand elders expressed when they rebuked their own young, that awareness of what incest can involve springs not from the child's experiences of its elders (which is the Freudian argument explicit in his sexual theories and his band of jealous young men) but from the elders' experiences of the young. It might be an unconscious childish situation: it is a *conscious* parental dilemma.

I think Freud is basically right, and that there is inherent in the family relationship, with its intimacy, its emotional exposure of one human being to another (no matter of what age), and in the possessive affections which characterize it, a situation potentially incestuous, giving rise to jealousies and tensions, and I think that the conquest of these is the first price to be paid for the maintenance of the human condition. I would not follow Freud in all the conclusions, some exceedingly strange, which he draws from this. He is wrong, to begin with, I imagine, in accepting the notion of a primitive horde from Darwin. Darwin was influenced by his contact with the Fuegians, and he never saw them save as a herd of wild animals. But the Fuegians or the Aborigines, though economically a food-gathering band or horde, are *socially* a strongly structured society whose members are disciplined even more than civilized peoples by things invisible. If we see this, if we understand that it is most probable that the first human societies were just as strongly structured, then we can understand that it was *adult* vision which saw both the dangers and temptations of incest, and which created the totemic institutions and other social divisions for the protection of the ignorant and hot-headed young, and therefore for the ultimate salvation of society.

I think that what was discovered was the choice between incest and love. The love which exists between parents and children is not of the order of sexual love and it is recognized by all, no matter what the status of the society to which they belong, as capable of being destroyed by lust. If the parent knows this out of experience, and at the same time foresees the future through which the child must be guided and helped, he (or she) must understand too that if he pursues the satisfaction of lust through his own offspring, he must by the act of incest directed downwards risk destroying that delicate relationship which is a source of inner spiritual stature as well as of social standing. In fact, incest is an act of self-destruction. If notwithstanding, the satisfaction of lust is embarked upon at the expense of the offspring, the parent must now turn one or more of his children into the object of temporary and probably secret intercourse, or 'espouse' it openly and so break with the legitimate partner, rousing in the process a hatred and jealousy which would make insecure the lives of both offenders, and render the task of caring for the rest of the family impossible. The family would dissolve, only the promiscuous sexual horde might conceivably take its place. Moreover the parent would have to face a future bereft of all those continuing elements of family and kinship which are even more important to primitive people than to civilized ones.

It is not simply that the element of love and tenderness would make doubly horrible the act of lust: that alone might be overborne. But man's mind works backwards and forwards along the dimension of time, seeing what has been, and what might be, and, before ever evil is committed, seeing all that might flow from one act of his loins. This transcendent vision (for that is what it is) is an act of the spirit. Man here is living in the spirit. He is thinking in the spirit. By virtue of the spirit, he sees what can be, and what need not be. He is free to choose. His vision ranges far beyond the pleasure of man and child in an act to which they might both consent, it searches far enough ahead to see what irreparable injury might be done not only to family and society, but to the spirit. The father sees how his own spirit would have been ruined had he been aware of incest in the family of *his* father; he conceives therefore what would just as easily transpire in his own. He knows what his own horror and rage would have been if his brother had lain with his mother. And in his spirit he shrinks from the moral horror that the deed would lay upon his soul, and conjure up in the souls of others. He is able to consider his neighbours. What would he think or say of them were he to discover such practices in the next hut? A deep troubled awareness of this or that aspect of the breaking of the taboo does not mean that incest directed downwards is never committed; but it does mean that no fully adult parent, or completely normal one, even in the most primitive society, and even in the absence of specific injunctions against it, could embark upon it without an angry consciousness of most of the consequences which would flow from it.

There is something remarkable, and essentially unnatural, in this ability man possesses to put himself sympathetically in the minds of others. The discovery of incest is man's first great moral leap, perhaps the moral leap by which he becomes man, for through it man realizes that he is no longer as the animals, and can never become as the animals again without abandoning his treasured human condition. Horror of incest could be horror of a dimly apprehended animal past. David Hume is right: in this sense, incest is a human discovery. The same act of spirit which reveals the meaning of incest to him makes it impossible for man to revert to the state of animal innocence before it. There is a significant point, in illustration of the argument that I am making, in what Malinowski says the Trobriand Islanders believe about the source of the sexual impulse. For them, 'the eyes are the primary motive of all sexual excitement'—'they are "that which makes us desire to copulate".' Lust of the eye in that sense is strictly human: it is absent from the animal situation, which is governed by other laws. It is an imaginative act.

Incest, then, is the poisoned spear directed at the very heart of the human situation. It is destructive of human stature and of the human order in which man discovers himself. It is condemned from within by the man committing it as much as from without by the law or the exogamic institution. In man's own consciousness (or, better, conscience) he sees the complete appropriateness of society's hatred for it. It appears as something so much against the Divine command or natural ordinance (and to primitive man these can appear as one) as to constitute a disturbance of the order of the universe, a disturbance which lets loose upon the world a series of unpredictable natural and social catastrophes. Not only personal sickness may fall upon the doer, but economic or other disaster, flood, tempest, loss of crops or of battles, upon the tribe. For these reasons also the incestuous wrongdoer is the hidden enemy at the heart of the world, ruining its harmony and calling down the divine wrath upon man, as the angels of the Lord called it down upon Sodom and Gomorrah.

CHAPTER 6

The Sense of the Sacred

I think we have to accept that the dread of incest is rooted in a great act of renunciation, and by that act the moral sense of man was born. This seems more probable an explanation than the effort to root it in, shall we say, the Oedipus complex, where the child, through a struggle between love and hostility towards its parents, breaks free of emotional dependence upon them and so of incestuous desires. I do not believe this is true: without parental disapproval how could they ever break free? I believe that the act of renunciation begins with the parents, and that this is borne out by an examination of primitive institutions directed against endogamy. These are most strongly oriented against any possibility of brother-sister incest, and since they could never have been invented by children, we must conclude that they are institutions which stem from tribal elders wise enough to see against what in their own natures the young must be protected, and aware that the parental renunciation cannot itself be maintained unless the ban upon incest extends to the siblings too.

Is it necessary to say however that in this the moral sense of man was born? I think this is a reasonable assumption. A moral sense is not born by the creation of temperamental idiosyncrasies in our infancy, but by the free choices of our maturity. Man—or let us, for the sake of convenience, say *primal* man, though in these things I do not believe we are so very different— finds himself in possession of desires or lusts of which his body seeks ease, but instead of seeking immediate relief as an animal would, he refrains and denies himself even in societies which plunge periodically into delirious orgy, and takes pride in this. He does so because he is able to remember the past events of his life and trace their relation to the visibly present world of things and imaginatively manipulate both past and present in order to construct a future. True, it is an imagined future, but it is also a possible one, for which his present acts can just as surely prepare, as repairing a spear and weaving a fishing net make possible the catch of fish in a tomorrow which has not yet come. The moment he becomes capable of manipulating the future in his head, primal man becomes capable of moral decisions too. If this new power of his were purely egotistic there would be no moral decisions other than those dictated by the pleasure-pain principle, which is to say that what would appear good for him in the future would be what he thought was going to give him pleasure. There is no morality however unless one renounces what is going to give one pleasure for fear it might give someone else pain. That same imaginative power which enables primal man to reassemble the elements of the past and present in an imagined future, also enables him to identify himself with other actors in the drama, and see the drama in their terms. This, it would seem, is precisely the act of identification which led to the cave drawings of Altamira and Lascaux, acts of identification so powerful that man is often sketched in no more than formally, while hunted beasts are caught with a haunting realism. If a hunter, turned cave-artist, can enter into the life of a beast with such power that it breathes pantingly again after perhaps thirty thousand years, are we to suppose that his power to reconstruct the lives of his fellow-tribesmen in his own mind was any the less? He must just as often and just as broodingly have dwelt upon the future days of his family as upon the morrow's hunting of the deer or the wild bulls.

What he discovers in himself, side by side with this power to manipulate the order of things in his mind, is an intense and burning will. It is this will which makes him the hunter, and he is aware that he is pitting his will and his cunning against those of his animal victims. On the chase he has many times seen how his intervention has caused an entire herd to start in panic flight: he has seen in the eyes of hunted creatures the whole constellation of things swirl into disaster. In the dark on his pallet in a hut he knows just what he can will. If he discovers this power in himself, he is of necessity bound to suspect its presence in any other seemingly purposive act which he witnesses—the tree which crashes in the compound, the river which overflows, the lightning which strikes the sacred tree. We are apt to describe his animism as a kind of ignorance; we should do better to understand that by it he witnesses to what he knows best—the spiritual dimension. He lives so much in the realm of willing, desiring, conceiving, scheming and concealing that he needs no persuasion to believe that what is most powerful in the life of himself and his tribe saturates the whole universe too.

It is necessary however to speak of ways in which things can go wrong with that natural order apart from the acts of his will. 'Go wrong' is anthropomorphic, of course. The hunter knows how things can go wrong with his chase; only after it is all over can he perceive, with time to think, where he failed himself. He knows that things can go wrong with the hunted creatures, and that they can destroy themselves as well as he destroy them through greed, stupidity, curiosity or stubbornness. He is ready to believe that the natural order may 'go wrong' and that the cause may lie with the malice of other beings—invisible ones such as demons, spirits of neglected ancestors, spirits of the game he has killed. Yet if so, he has probably contributed to that situation by his failure to flatter or appease the spirits in order to mitigate their hostility. Yet there is another sense in which the natural order may go wrong—that man has failed *in himself*, and *before* himself and must make some atonement, if atonement is at all possible. How atone? Primal man has already recognized sexual renunciation as the great act of withdrawal or surrender. It is deeply associated with acts of propitiation directed towards hostile spirits; equally it is perhaps man's first positive moral act. Hence the universality of sacrifice—even of that most precious, the first-fruits of hunt or harvest, or the first-born son. The hope which directs the sacrifice is that the initial harmony shall be restored by it. The renunciation which has set things right for himself is to set things right for the natural order too.

The sense that nature can be deformed by human misdeeds runs deep through human history. Only our own times find the idea odd. Horror, in *Julius Caesar*, is heightened by Cassius' speech to Casca in the night street scene:

> *You are dull, Casca,*
> *And those sparks of life, that should be in a Roman,*
> *You do want, or else you use not.*
> *You look pale, and gaze, and put on fear,*
> *And cast yourself in wonder,*
> *To see the strange impatience of the heavens:*
> *But if you would consider the true cause,*
> *Why all these fires, why all these gliding ghosts,*
> *Why birds and beasts, from quality and kind,*
> *Why old men, fools, and children calculate,*
> *Why all these things change from their ordinance,*
> *Their natures, and pre-formed faculties,*
> *To monstrous quality; why you shall find,*
> *That Heaven hath infus'd them with these Spirits,*
> *To make them instruments of fear, and warning,*
> *Unto some monstrous state.*

And Lennox says to Macbeth just before the discovery of Macduff's murder:

> *The night has been unruly:*
> *Where we lay, our Chimneys were blown down,*
> *And, as they say, lamentings heard in the air;*
> *Strange screams of death,*
> *And prophesying, with accents terrible,*
> *Of dire combustion, and confused events,*
> *New hatched to the woeful time.*
> *The obscure bird clamoured the live-long night.*
> *Some say, the earth was feverous,*
> *And did shake.*

133

In truth men have always found it hard to believe that their own terrible wills for good or evil would not leave their mark upon the universe. 'The heavens themselves blaze forth the death of princes.' Nor can they easily believe that the still more terrible will of God or gods is not equally made evident in the behaviour or misbehaviour of natural things. A meteor or shooting star during the vigil of the Spartan ephors was sufficient to suspend a king for an offence against a deity.

When the wills of men and gods work openly or secretly throughout the natural order—what is not holy or sacred? It is almost impossible to exclude any aspect of any activity from the exercise, or the emanations of, divine or quasi-divine power. And it seems therefore that so powerful in man is the consciousness of the spiritual realm in which he lives, that in primitive societies the whole of life is saturated with a sense of the sacred. In fact, as I think we must acknowledge from the anthropological writings of Durkheim or Levy-Bruhl, a primitive society is often also a church. It is not simply a social institution, it is a sacred one, and no one born in that social institution can imagine how it can survive without the performance of the sacred duties which membership imposes. The society has a supernatural origin and a supernatural end, and may even believe itself to play a creative rôle in the maintenance of the supernaturally established order round it. Even so frightful a record of human sacrifice as that of the Aztecs witnesses all the same to a sense of responsibility for the universe. Unless the sun was fed with living human hearts it would cease to shine and the human race come to an end.

On this theme Charles Mountford said this about the Australian aborigines: 'Just as the links of the aborigines with their past are strong and enduring, so is their relationship with and their control of the world round them. It is the aborigines, by their increase ceremonies, who cause the animals to reproduce, the trees to blossom and bear fruit, and the grasses to bring forth seed. Because they are responsible for the creation of life, the aborigines do not destroy it beyond their immediate requirements. . . The close identification of man with his environment also governs the ownership of aboriginal land. The tribal boundaries of each family were determined by their semi-human forebears, who not only created the natural features of the country—the rocks, trees, and streams, but also the myths, songs and ceremonies, which belong to those natural features. It would be impossible therefore, for a family of Kangaroo men to possess the tribal lands of, say, the Emu men.'[1] There we see the sacred society set in what is essentially a sacred, super-naturally created land, with the present inhabitants sharing the creative rôle of their semi-human totemic forebears, such as the Wawilak women.

It seems appropriate therefore, at this point, to look at the Intichiuma ceremonies of the aborigines in which the creative function is fulfilled. This will lead to a more general considera-tion of the sacred motif in primitive society.

In the Arunta tribes, which occupy ancient tribal grounds straddling the McDonnell Ranges of Central Australia, the name Intichiuma is given to those ceremonies, associated with certain totems, which have an economic or social purpose. When it is the intention of the ceremonies to ensure a supply of the animal which forms the totemic emblem, then we are surely in the presence of the belief of the aborigines that they play a creative rôle in their universe. Spencer and Gillen described the rain-making ceremony that they witnessed in these ranges. The per-forming headman wore a head-dress of hair string completely covered by white down, which fell over his shoulders and his chest. One horizontal bar of down, stuck to his skin, passed across his stomach, and vertical bars decorated his back, one each side of his spine. His head-dress was tipped with cockatoo feathers, and bunches of hawk feathers hung in a girdle round his waist. A spear-thrower in hand, the headman squatted on the ground in front of a few old men in the tribe who sang a magical refrain and struck the earth with a stone as they chanted. While this was going on, the headman rose to a stooping position. He struck out with the thrower, and moved it backwards and forwards. Then he quivered his body and

[1] *Brown Men and Red Sand*, p 187.

turned his head from side to side like an anxious animal picking up a scent. At intervals he stretched his body up as if attempting to rise into the sky like the mythical cloud men who went into the sky and formed clouds from which the first rain came.[1] Spencer and Gillen do not tell us whether the rain-making ceremony was successful. Charles Mountford, journeying among the Mann and Musgrave Ranges of Central Australia, described one that was. The magical core of these ceremonies, he says, is a disc of pearl shell, one of many which are picked up on the beaches of north-western Australia and traded inwards to finish up on the coast two thousand miles across the continent. The shells are rubbed against stones in the course of rain-making ceremonies and so slowly get ground down and down until they are no larger than florins at the end of the journey. The pearl shells, or *ringili*, are, the aborigines believe, 'impregnated with the *kuranita* (life essence) of water' and it is only necessary to project that *kuranita* into the air in order to make clouds grow. Mountford's rain-maker joked about it and said that he would have to be careful how he carried out the ritual, lest they were all washed away, but another black-fellow reassured the whites —it was easy to stop the rain by sprinkling ashes on the pearl shell and burying it.

The ceremony took place out of sight of the women. First, the rain-maker, to the chants of the men, 'squirted a stream of chewed native tobacco . . . on a flat stone, then rubbed the edge of the *ringili* across it, sucking the shell at intervals and spitting into the sky'.[2] The performer left the line of men, and walked across an open flat 'lightly touching the tops of the mulga grass with the pearl shell'.[3] When he returned to the ceremonial ground, he put blood and grass on the flat stone, and rubbed the shell there, and sucked it and spat into the air. When the ceremony was over, the shell was hung on a low mulga tree and left there. Mountford interpreted the ceremony in terms of sympathetic magic. The chewed tobacco smelt like rain; sucking extracted the *kuranita*, or powerful essence of rain, from the

[1] *The Northern Tribes of Central Australia*, p. 286.
[2] *Brown Men and Red Sand*, p. 139.   [3] Ibid.

shell, and spitting projected it into the sky where it might begin its work. The creamy mulga grass looked like clouds, so that touching the grass with the shell showed the sky what it ought to do. The freely swinging shell 'beckoned the rain to the place of the ceremony'.[1] Mountford's rain-maker enjoyed a spectacular success: he produced the rain just when they needed it most badly, in face of a dangerous water shortage in the desert, and it fell 'in early September, quite out of season, the normal times being between November and March'.[2]

Spencer and Gillen tell of a special ceremony performed by the members of the snake totemic group. The old headman of the group was the performer. His body was decorated with red and yellow ochre and he wore on his head a banner-like device decorated with plumes of cockatoo feathers. In his outstretched hands he held pieces of sharpened bone which were, presumably, to represent the fangs of the snakes. He knelt on the ground and one companion on each side took a piece of bone, pinched up the skin of the arm and thrust the bone clean through it. This painful act must have represented the serpent bite. Holding his arms, each assistant sang—

Lirri watthai umpai
Lara nalari tjinta

—and, as was the case of the words of chants in all the ceremonies, the meaning of these had been lost. When the chanting was over, the bones were withdrawn and the ceremony ended. After the ceremony, when snakes have become plentiful again as a result of the totemic magic, men who do not belong to the snake group (to whom, of course, snake-eating is taboo) go out and catch snakes and bring them to the old performer, saying, 'See, here are snakes'. Some snake fat is presented to the old man, who rubs his arms and says, 'You *eat*—all of you'. This is a form of public acknowledgement of the chief's snake-making powers.

In general, this can be said about the ceremonies, that the members of a totem group perform them in order to secure an

[1] Ibid., p. 140.   [2] Ibid., p. 151.

increase in their totemic animal, plant, or power. But this magic is not exercised on their own behalf (except in the spiritual sense that an increase in the numbers of their own animal or plant is a strengthening of the totem and leads to an increase in its prestige), for they do not eat their totem, or at least only sacramentally on rare occasions. On the other hand, the performer of the ceremony must eat of the totem now and then, in ceremonial manner, or he would be unable to perform his magic. The striking thing is that these powers of totem members are exercised for the general economic good, in which, in the case of their own totem animal, they cannot possibly share. A failure on the part of any one group to do its work could lead to a general economic collapse.

The creation rôle of the totem groups which is so manifest in these ceremonies, of which I have given one or two examples out of a great abundance and variety, is only one instance of how the lives of the natives are caught up in a supernatural scheme, the original powers of which have in some part descended to them. But this touches no more than the fringe of the native ecclesia, as we shall see.

Among the Murngin people, as among so many other aboriginal peoples, the clan totems are thought to dwell in the clan water hole, and upon the death of a man his spirit goes back to the clan totem to await reincarnation. The mourning and burial rites are designed to assist him in that process, and to expedite it. If the dying native is capable of it, he may even dance his totem death dance to warn the clan totem of his coming. The new-born child comes from the well as a spirit, though in the well it has the appearance of a small fish. The spirit comes to the father first, and asks the father in a dream where it may find its mother. The father points her out, and the child then enters the mother's womb. It is to the father, first of all, that news about the new birth comes, and this manner of intimating conception is accepted by everyone. Professor Warner gives this interesting autobiographical report about it from a native:

'I had a nice dream the other night. I dreamed that a boy child walked past all the other humpies [Australian white term for native huts] in the camp and kept coming until he got to my house. He beat on the bark wall. He called out, "Father! Father! Where are you?"

' "Here I am."

' "Where is Mother?"

'I told him and wakened up. I thought to myself, "True". Yesterday I went fishing with my wife at the creek. I went up one side of the creek and she went up the other. By and by a bream fish came up and took her hook. He came up to it easily and quietly. My wife did not have to pull on the line, for he came in to her like he wanted to. My *mielk* [woman] was standing in the water only up to her ankles. He came up to her even though she was in the shallow water. Then he stopped quickly, shook himself against her leg, broke the line, and went back into deep water. We did not see him again. I came across to her; I said, "What was that?" She said, "A bream fish." I said, "What did he do?" She told me. She said, "My father went fishing like this when my little brother was born; I think this fish shook against my leg for that." I said, "Oh you know that?" "Yes." "You remember my dream I told you about?" She said, "Yes, that's what I think. I won't menstruate any longer now because that baby fish is inside me." '[1]

As the child, incarnate spirit of the clan totem, grows up, the highly ritualistic and institutional life controls him more and more completely. The moiety in which he finds himself governs those he may know in play in childhood, as well as those he may ultimately marry. It ties him to uncles, to whom he must make gifts and before whom he must show goodwill in anticipation of eventual marriage favours. When he is circumcised and moved for ever from the control of the women, then his real tribal membership begins. He has entered a sacred realm, full knowledge of which is kept from the female population of the tribe. As he grows older he receives new initiations, which advance him in status, for he may not view certain totems until he is bearded, and he may not be initiated into the final totemic mysteries until he is an old man. But not to be initiated when

[1] *A Black Civilisation*, pp. 21-2.

the proper time comes is to be an outcast, or at least to watch the younger creep past one. It is unthinkable, for the Murngin man is securely tied to the spiritual ladder which all his forebears have walked. For the older men, the ceremonies fill nearly all their lives. They are the high priests of the mysteries. Spencer and Gillen made a record (in 1901) of some eighty-eight ceremonies performed in a matter of eight weeks, some of them of the utmost elaboration.

The legend of the two Wawilak women which Professor Warner described, and on which I have already drawn, is re-enacted every year: it goes on for many weeks, with all-night sessions of dramatic intensity. It is, as someone has said, a great Wagnerian drama, but unlike such a drama, not simply a dramatic spectacle, but a magic ritual, failure to repeat which would bring disaster down on the tribe. By repetition, on the other hand, the natives ensure that the supernatural power which brought them into being continues to exercise its authority among them, and communicates to them that *kuranita* or vital strength, or essence without which they cannot continue to thrive. 'It is believed that if, through any ritually impure act, the Wongar totem snake should be angered, he would come out and swallow the earth, and a flood would come at the same time.'[1] And again, Professor Warner sums it up thus, 'The society is disciplined by threat of what will happen to nature, the provider, if the members of the group misbehave. This brings on an identification of the social organization with nature, and they are treated as one and expressed as such in the rituals.'[2]

The last great religious rite within the community takes place at a man's death. Stage by stage the man has gone through the initiations which have raised him in status within the community, and brought him to closer communion with the sacred totemic spirits. Now, at last, at his death he rejoins those spirits, from whom, after a lapse of time, he will be reincarnated in a new child of the tribe.

Where a birth, especially a first birth, is a matter of great

[1] Ibid., p. 384.　　　[2] Ibid., p. 411.

rejoicing, because it proves the tribal compatibility of the young couple, a death produces stillness and fear, unless of the very, very old. Deaths are held to be due to sorcery and the relatives of the dead express their intention of taking revenge upon the murderers. No one is certain who may be accused. But as a man is dying, on the other hand, his relatives gather round him and sing the song cycles which will so perfectly declare the totemic man that he is that he will find his ancestors without trouble, avoid the conspiracies of the evil spirits which lie in wait for him, and go straight to his totem well. This is the desired consummation.

The body of the dead man is painted with the same totemic design which would be placed upon a boy of that clan about to be circumcised, in order that the ancestral spirits can recognize him. The hair of the dead man is plucked out to be woven into sacred hair belts. The mourning relatives gash their thighs. Then, with fire sticks, the spirit of the dead man is driven into the jungle so that he may finish with the living and find his way back to his ancestors. After a long sequence of totemic songs of mourning, the man is buried, or placed upon a platform in the trees. Sometimes his body is inspected after a short time for signs of sorcery: were these to be proved appropriate vengeance would be taken. Neither the burial nor the placing of the body upon a platform is final. The intention is that everything perishable shall perish and only the bones shall be left. After several months have elapsed, the body is exhumed, the bones carefully cleaned; ceremonial fires are lit to screen the operation and to cleanse the air. Apart from a few small bones kept as memorials, and carried around in a pouch, the remainder may be wrapped in paper bark and placed in the fork of a tree some distance from the camp. There they are watched by a keeper of the bones and when dried and clean they are covered with red ochre, a surrogate for blood in many primitive ceremonies, placed in a paper bark receptacle, and brought back into camp. They may be carried around in the tribe for a while, but finally the bones are pounded and placed in a hollow log coffin and buried with great ceremony. In some tribes the bones are buried so that the skull faces towards the ancestral grounds.

The last great rite of passage has been performed, and with what abundant energy and ceremony this passage from *Brown Men and Red Sand* best tells us. Charles Mountford is speaking of a party returning from the first burial, and, when they reached them, scattering branches over the mourners who stayed behind:

'Instantly pandemonium broke loose. The sounds of mourning rose to a high-pitched wail; the men sobbed heartbrokenly; twenty or thirty women, screaming loudly, were either throwing themselves on the ground with dull, sickening thuds, or vehemently lacerating their scalps with digging sticks. It was a scene of uncontrolled grief and mass hysteria. Yet, in contrast with that unhappy, sorrowing throng were two rows of men lying face downwards, their bodies rigid, their arms locked about each other, and hands tightly clenched. Then came the most curious and unexplainable part of the whole strange ceremony, something which suggested a possible belief in a future life: the resurrection of the "dead" man. The living men disentangled the stiff, rigid bodies one by one, turning them face upwards, bending the trunks, unclenching the hands, vigorously rubbing the bodies and limbs, and roughly pulling the ears. Slowly each "dead" man came to life; his body and limbs lost their rigidity, his hands relaxed, his eyes opened, until eventually he sat up and mourned with the rest. As the ceremony progressed, more and more "dead" men were brought to life; the sounds of the mourning died down; the women throwing themselves on the ground fewer and fewer, until only one figure remained. She was the mother of Namana (the dead man). Her yellow ochre-covered body, streaked with the blood that flowed from her wounded scalp, was so exhausted she could scarcely raise herself to a standing position to cast herself once more on the ground.'[1]

Enough has been said to show that one of the most primitive peoples in existence, technically so poorly equipped that it has been said of them that aboriginal women, with only carrying dishes, grinding stones and digging sticks as tools, are able to live in the barren desert, enjoys nevertheless a life so com-

[1] *Brown Men and Red Sand*, p. 127.

pletely bound up with the sacred and supernatural that it is impossible to conceive how the social and economic aspects of the lives of the members (to say nothing of the sexual) could ever be disentangled from them. And what has been said of them, the aborigines, could be said with the same truth of the Trobrianders, for whom too, birth is reincarnation of spirit children whose voices can be heard crying in the waves off the shore at the still of night. And so throughout the whole range of primitive peoples. Modern anthropological research would place the religious beliefs of all these peoples at the heart of their social systems. The religion and the polis are, in that sense, one, as they were in the Greek city states.

It is quite easy to see that if the tribal life, a small portion of which I have described, is sacred, then it can easily happen in time that he who comes to represent the tribe, or lead the tribe, can be held to incarnate the sacredness of the tribe. Among the aborigines, the holiest are the hale old men. Spencer and Gillen grumbled that everything in the tribe seemed to be arranged for their comfort and convenience but their power was due to their sacredness, or their closeness to the sacred mysteries, which is much the same thing.

And around the killing of the sacred king, and of his relation to fertility rites, Sir James Frazer built up the great theme of *The Golden Bough*. And we know that in our own times an aura of holiness may still surround a king or queen, despite all the process of democratization. In the coronation of the British monarch this holiness is imparted in a sacred ceremony in which the monarch is anointed with holy oil by the highest religious dignitary in the land. Hardly beyond living memory the king's touch, his priestly or magical touch, was presumed to heal people of scrofula, or the king's evil.

Sacredness attaches even more to that other mediator between the people and the highest powers of the universe—the priest. Dr. E. O. James, in *The Nature and Function of the Priesthood*, has described the priesthood as 'the official organ for maintaining a state of equilibrium between the sacred and the secular. Through the exercise of its prescribed techniques and disciplines it has been a stabilizing force in the social structure and in the religious life of the community by establishing efficacious relations with the transcendental power believed to control the universe and human affairs and destinies. Thus, in its several capacities it has become the dynamic centre of the sacred order with far-reaching effects in the body politic.'[1]

This is not the moment to decide whether man is right or wrong in assuming that his society has any connection with the sacred, either because it is sacred in itself, or has priests and rulers divinely appointed. Man may be quite wrong in believing this. The point is that throughout ancient times men did believe this, and in the modern world men still do. Even those who accept materialistic interpretations of history are nevertheless ready to affirm that the societies they favour, or create, are incarnations of a historical process—a new name for God. Society, for man, is not *merely* an artifact: it is not just a social contract adhered to as one might adhere to a commercial one: it is not the striking of a bargain with one's neighbours. It is, in one way or another, in the Jewish way, or the aboriginal way, or the Greek way, or the Persian way, or the Egyptian way, an institution deriving its authority from the greater than human, the greater than nature—'the transcendental power believed to control the universe and human affairs'. It is not given to man by nature, but ordained by God for man: it comes from above and not from below, and man's human condition is bound up with its continuing health. By human society man is pulled out, and kept out, of nature, and given the spiritual freedom through which he can acquire a history. Even if man turns out to be totally wrong in his ideas of the sacred, at least he would be right in what he implies about human society by the use of the term—that human society is not as other things, that it holds such a special place for man that without it he could not endure. It is the cradle in which he discovers his humanity, and the shield by which he protects it.

[1] London, 1955, p. 13.

CHAPTER 7

The Tongues of Men and of Angels

I

The two Wawilak women, on their journey from the south to Northern Australia, named the places they passed. They had the gift of tongues, and in the various stories told of them, this primeval gift of naming, this Genesis theme, ranks very high. Even the most primitive of men, it seems, recognize the uniqueness of the human ability to speak, and how it shuts them off from the animals, and the peculiar power that it enables them to exercise over their environment. Names, they quickly learned, give men power over the things named, and for that reason the power of naming rouses an almost superstitious fear in the minds of savages, at which fear the civilized man looks with undeserved condescension, as though this were another example of backwardness. Yet the savage is right, and the civilized man, who treats so many of his gifts lightly, has simply forgotten what is involved in the power to name. Let me give examples. A doctor, faced with an emergency, needs a bottle of a particular drug from the shelf in his dispensary, but he has forgotten its name. He can say to the dispenser, 'Fetch me a bottle'. But any bottle might come, and the chances are that it would be useless. Or all bottles might come, and he would have to search through the lot to find the drug. He may remember the colour of the bottle, and say, 'Fetch me the brown bottle of drugs'. But there may be many such bottles.

K
145

He still has not got hold of the drug. Then he remembers its name and says, 'Fetch me the calomel'. And immediately it is brought to him. The power of naming is power over one's environment. It might be argued that what I have described here is simply knowledge—that the power to name equals the power to know. However, it is not so. No one need doubt that had the doctor himself gone to his dispensary he would have gone straight to the right bottle whether it had borne a label or not. The power to name is the power to *manipulate* knowledge: it is the power to create a universe of discrete objects, and to codify it, and communicate knowledge of that universe to others by conventional symbols.

Man's environment includes people, so that power to name includes power over other men too. Take this imaginary case: a child has been attacked on her way to school and robbed of her dinner money. She complains to the headmistress, who assembles the school to search for witnesses. 'Who saw this?' she asks. Several hands shoot up. 'Do you know who did it?' 'It was a man,' a child ventures, and others nod. It certainly was a man, but in a great city there may be a million or two men. 'It was Charlie Jones down our street!' shouts a boy, and immediately the matter is solved. The power to name is the power to identify, and identification gives the mind a hold upon the object identified, even if that hold is not physical but only memory. The whole democratic system of voting by putting a cross against a candidate's name, or a party list, involves the power of naming: no indication of choice is possible without it. 'Romeo, Romeo, wherefore art thou Romeo?' Juliet cries. The name evokes the lover and all the life in which he is set and the circumstances by which he is surrounded, and breathes a mysterious power to the soul. To name inwardly, to call up a name, is to evoke some image or recollection of the person, to point the mind at that person, and there are times when no one wants that, even understandably dreads it. Part of the process of prayer involves just this power to name. It is because all men share the power of naming that we no longer attach special importance to it, at least until we come to an examination

paper or some similar test which floors us. Where all men
equally are endowed it is human nature not to value the endowment specially high. But for the aborigine who asks of the
stranger, 'Where is water?' and who receives the reply, 'At
Yurkyurk water hole!'—the power of naming is life itself.

Language has always been recognized as that gift which distinguishes man from the animals, and many noble and profound
things have been said about it, but even so it seems to me that
much remains to be said. I do not know whether it can be said
unless we turn back first to some of the nineteenth-century
speculations which associated human language with the cries of
birds and animals. It was Darwin who set the fashion. In *The
Descent of Man* he elaborated his reasons for applying the arguments of *The Origin of Species* to man. His intention was to prove
that 'man bears within his frame the indelible stamp of his
lowly origin' and that it necessarily followed therefore that
'there is no fundamental difference between man and the
higher mammals in their mental faculties'. Man has no special
equipment, Darwin's argument runs, his powers are simply
developments of those which mammals and many lesser creatures also possess. The differences which we are apt to believe
are differences of kind, are really no more than differences of
degree. 'It has been asserted that man alone is capable of
progressive improvement,' he wrote, 'that he alone makes use
of tools or fire, domesticates other animals, or possesses property;
that no animal has the power of abstraction, or of forming
general concepts, is self-conscious and comprehends itself; that
no animal employs language; that man alone has a sense of
beauty, is liable to caprice, has the feeling of gratitude, mystery,
etc.; believes in God, or is endowed with a conscience.'[1] Darwin,
in rejecting such claims, sought to show that all the higher
animals including man 'have some few instincts in common.
All have the same senses, intuitions, and sensations—similar
passions, affections, and emotions, even the more complex ones,
such as jealousy, suspicions, emulation, gratitude, and mag-
nanimity; they practise deceit and are revengeful; they are

[1] *Descent of Man*, Edn. 1922, p. 121.

sometimes susceptible to ridicule, and even have a sense of humour; they feel wonder and curiosity; they possess the same faculties of imitation, attention, deliberation, choice, memory, imagination, the association of ideas, and reason, though in very different degrees. The individuals of the same species graduate in intellect from absolute imbecility to high excellence. They are also liable to insanity, though far less often than in the case of man. Nevertheless, many authors have insisted that man is divided by an insuperable barrier from all the lower animals in his mental faculties.'[1] So strongly does Darwin press the identity of man and animals, that the difficulty is to know how precisely, except by physiology, man is to be distinguished from other primates.

Darwin's method is extremely anecdotal. He tells many stories of how animals have from time to time improvised tools —of how monkeys use stones to open nuts, or orang-utans use levers, or tame elephants use branches of trees as fly swats, or baboons use stones as weapons. Such examples are well-attested and unexceptionable. They reveal that an animal often shows an ability at improvisation in a moment of difficulty or danger. Man too possesses this ability to improvise, but his tool-making techniques are rather more than that, and ought not to be dismissed so easily. They involve the steady growth of an ability to fashion increasingly exact and specialized tools and instruments in an ever-widening range, and with an ever-improving technique, through the growth of a professional tradition involving in the end a widespread division of labour. We find evidence of human tool-making going back for about half a million years and have some reason to think that it was even at the first associated with the use of language. There is just no evidence of animal perseverance in the making of tools and dwellings over that range of time—or any range of time!— except where the activities are purely instinctive, as in the nests the mason martins fabricate from mortar scooped up at the edge of a pond. Of development or improvement, there is no evidence. What then are we witnessing in the human case? If

[1] Ibid., p. 120.

the faculties are identical, what factor accounts for so vast a difference in results? Man's tool-making power appears to be something greater than improvisation in face of a visible emergency: he has the power to anticipate in imagination, and with extraordinary exactness, the type of situation with which he will be faced in the future and to fabricate tools and other artifacts to meet that type of situation—consider for example the primitive hunter with his spears, nets, bolas, traps and ropes to bind his prey, or the savage fisherman with his nets, lines, hooks, bait, gaff, and fish baskets—and the extent of man's imaginative preparation for situations yet to arrive becomes clear. Such tool-making power appears to belong only to man, and to him only because he has the power to think conceptually. But Darwin asserts that the power to form mental concepts is a property of animals too. 'When a dog sees another dog at a distance, it is often clear that he perceives that it is a dog in the abstract; for when he gets nearer his whole manner suddenly changes, if the other dog be a friend. A recent writer [Mr. Hookham] remarks, that in all such cases it is a pure assumption to assert that the mental act is not essentially of the same nature in the animal as in man.'[1] And Darwin goes on to tell how his own terrier could be induced to search around for an animal to be hunted if he cried out to it in an eager voice, 'Hi, hi, where is it?' His terrier must have had therefore some 'idea or concept' that game was there to be discovered and hunted! It might be possible to analyse Darwin's examples of intelligent animal behaviour according to the stimulus-response theory of behaviourism. If one does not, and accepts that here there is something either identical with, or close to, man's power to think conceptually, then the result is not more illumination, but less, for it still remains necessary to show why, when both men and animals are equipped with identical powers, the product of the human use of them is so *qualitatively* different from the animal product.

The discussion which Darwin promotes is, in fact, quite poverty-stricken, in view of the vastness and importance of the

---

[1] Ibid., pp. 126-7. This seems not to be a process of abstraction at all, but an example of increasingly exact recognition.

problem. This is very obvious in his discussion of animal and human self-consciousness. He admits that an animal has no self-consciousness in the human sense. 'But how can we feel sure that an old dog with an excellent memory and some power of imagination, as shewn by his dreams, never reflects on his past pleasures and pains in the chase? And this would be a form of consciousness. On the other hand, as Büchner has remarked, how little can the hard-worked wife of a degraded Australian savage, who uses very few abstract words, and cannot count above four, exert her self-consciousness, or reflect on the nature of her own existence?'[1] We have seen enough, in the light of anthropological research, to doubt whether this description of an Australian aborigine woman is an exhaustive one: her self-consciousness is deeper than Darwin imagined, and potentially of the same quality as Darwin's own. And as for the self-consciousness of his dog, Darwin is just making guesses.

Such examples serve to show how Darwin consistently writes down the human equipment and writes up the animal, in order to place man as firmly as possible within the sphere of nature. And in nothing is this determination more clear than in his treatment of language. Does language distinguish man from the lower animals, Darwin asks? Surely not, when the *Cebus azarae* in Paraguay can make six distinct sounds, and the dog can bark in four or five distinct tones, each of which can be given a special meaning! 'That which distinguishes man from the lower animals is not the understanding of articulate sounds, for, as everyone knows, dogs understand many words and sentences. In this respect they are at the same stage of development as infants, between the ages of ten and twelve months, who understand many words and short sentences, but cannot yet utter a single word. It is not the mere articulation which is our distinguishing character, for parrots and other birds possess this power. Nor is it the mere capacity of connecting definite sounds with definite ideas; for it is certain that some parrots, which have been taught to speak, connect unerringly words with things, and persons with events. The lower animals

[1] Ibid., pp. 127-8

differ from man solely in his almost infinitely larger power of associating together the most diversified sounds and ideas; and this obviously depends on the high development of his mental powers.'[1]

Darwin then, having planted the origins of human language in the cries of lower creatures, goes on to liken the growth and development of language itself to an evolution. 'The formation of different languages and of distinct species, and the proofs that both have been developed through a gradual process, are curiously parallel.' There is a 'survival of the fit' among languages and 'a language, like a species, when once extinct, never, as Sir C. Lyell remarks, reappears. The same language never has two birth-places. Distinct languages may be crossed or blended together. We see variability in every tongue, and new words are continually cropping up; but as there is a limit to the powers of the memory, single words, like whole languages, gradually become extinct. . . The survival or preservation of certain favoured words in the struggle for existence is natural selection.'[2] Both the idea of language as a complication of animal cries, and the idea of language as an organism subject to natural selection did a great disservice to the science of linguistics, and to the task of understanding man.

I have dealt with this at some length in order to show the poverty of Darwin's treatment of the differences between human and animal mental activity. How threadbare much of Darwin's evidence is, and how obviously untested! How extraordinary that such an important point as self-consciousness should be dismissed in a few anecdotes. So let it be said now, if it has not been said before, that the behaviour of domestic pets, animals and birds is dubious evidence of the mental capacities of lower animals. Darwin, for instance, was fond of watching his dog, and the dog is an animal of high intelligence, but one which has deserted its natural state and cleaved to man: under human pressures and out of love for man it has submitted to a discipline which is wholly unnatural: meekly it allows itself to be pomaded, trimmed, cleaned, decked out with collars and even

[1] Ibid., p. 131.   [2] Ibid., pp. 138-9.

muzzles, and elects to accept a life of sexual austerity worthy of a monastic order, and sometimes an almost total withdrawal from its kind in favour of moving in the sphere of the human. Craving affection, naturally submissive, incredibly imitative, it is almost a different creature! Almost! For were the human demands to be withdrawn, and all dogs to be left wild, the dog would revert to its primitive state. It appears to possess no initiatives of its own to do for itself what has been done for it by man, or even to preserve what has been done, nor can we imagine that natural selection would enable it to move in the direction it has taken under its enslavement to man. And if, on the fringe of man's life, and craving his affection and company, it has picked up the meaning of just a handful of words (to it, not words, but *sounds*) that concern its own life, I do not see that it is safe to argue from this the virtual identity of the powers of man and the animals in respect of language. And, in any case, we really know little about the power of a dog's understanding: a tone of voice often seems more important to it than the actual words spoken; a general air of bustle conveys meanings just as quickly as words. But if we accept with Darwin that it understands whole sentences, there is little to be gained by comparing its situation with the situation of a year-old baby. In this respect, Darwin said, dogs 'are at the same stage of development as infants, between the ages of ten and twelve months, who understand many words and short sentences, but cannot yet utter a single word.' A *stage of development* implies a process—the possibility, even the certainty, of development; but what capacity the dog has now for understanding speech, it had half a million years ago on its first partnership with man; it has never shown signs of getting past this stage, whereas for the baby, speechlessness really *is* a stage, for that same baby within another twelve months will be talking, and a few years later writing, and (if Darwin was observing his own children) thirty or forty years later still compiling a memoir of its father. In one case there is no development: absolute limits appear to be set; in the other case it is almost infinite. And what conceivable weight are we to attach to the articulation of a parrot, except that other beings than man can articulate their sounds? That alone does not make language. For every parrot which shows the sense to say 'Good morning' in the morning, and 'Good night' at night, one can produce a score which will reel off at demand or inconsequentially a string of gibberish of which they understand nothing at all. They are repeating sounds which they have been induced to imitate in return for lumps of sugar.

It hardly seems worthy of so great a scientist to relate a few trivial examples and then to close the case. 'The lower animals differ from man solely in his almost infinitely larger power of associating together the most diversified sounds and ideas . . .' Darwin wrote.[1] What perplexed, struggling human millennia, savage and civilized, are dismissed by the adverb 'solely'! And yet should Darwin be right in every particular, and mammals and other animals be shown to share with man the richness of his emotional life, the profundity of his spiritual being, and his marvellous powers of conceptual thinking, the mystery would be deeper still. Then we should be called upon to explain why the animal world has done nothing despite these gifts to escape enslavement to nature, and man has done so much. What would be true in such a case would be that man and the animal kingdom were both presented with the keys to the spiritual world, but only man had used them.

II

There are three theories concerning the origin of human speech which have enjoyed special popularity. They have been described respectively as the 'bow-wow', the 'pooh-pooh' and the 'ding-dong' theories. The *bow-wow* theory argues that language is onomatopoeic—that the child calls a dog a 'bow-wow' and a cow a 'moo-cow' for the same reason that we call a cuckoo after the sound it makes. There are plenty of words in every language which are evocative of the noises of nature, or of human activities, and this theory has much strength. Man is

[1] Ibid., p. 131.

nothing if not imitative and imitative words are easy to invent, to learn and to repeat. Yet we have to remember that even onomatopoeia is governed by conventions. Dr. William J. Entwistle in *Aspects of Language* (1953) explains that 'Thus both Lat. *cachinnare* and Russ. *chochotat* are excellent imitations in sound of that which we imitate to our satisfaction by *guffaw*.'[1] The *pooh-pooh* theory bases itself on the familiar fact that under stress we utter relatively meaningless exclamations: these are natural sounds, expressions of pain and joy or surprise, which have no particular meaning and, though speech, are with difficulty contained within the conventions of a language. The difficulty about natural expressions like (to use English examples) *pshaw* or *pish*, *tut-tut*, *ahem*, *oh!* and *ah!* is that they continue to exist in primitive completeness and show no inclination to become words at all. We render them with difficulty in writing, and of the exclamations above only *oh!* and *ah!* are at all adequately rendered.

The third theory, a typical German one—it originated with Professor Heyse of Berlin in the last century and was popularized by Max Müller—is to the effect that nearly everything that is struck gives out a sound. 'Man was at the outset a kind of bell . . . when an idea struck him he naturally rang.' Man's body must, in other words, express in sounds what the object or experience calls forth in him—a highly mystical theory, which really falls back upon the argument that there is a natural harmony between objects and sounds, and that words therefore are not arbitrary, or conventional, but in a sense inevitable. Some evidence for this can be found in the existence of closely related words in the Indo-European languages, as though basic human experiences bring forth the same basic words.

Yet there are other theories than these. One, called the 'yo-he-ho' theory, really argues that certain physical exertions produce vocal reflexes—the running man pants, the labouring man grunts, the hammering man sings rhythmically, and so does the rower. This is related to the 'sing-song' theory which argues that language comes from rhythmic chants and songs. These are

[1] Op. cit., p. 18.

somewhat fanciful perhaps, and there is more to the gesture theory of language (which is also doomed to carry a nursery tag —it is called the 'ta-ta' theory). When we form the word 'long' we are actually pushing the tongue far forward, and the lips slightly forward—we are elongating our speech organs so that the word 'long' is a kind of gesture of length. 'Round', on the other hand, compels a circular movement of the tongue within the mouth, while 'stop' really compels an explosive bite of tongue against the palate to begin with, and then of firmly closed lips to form 'p.' This too can be analysed very easily as a gesture equivalent to biting something off very firmly. My examples are very simple ones, but they serve to illustrate a theory which has been worked out with a great wealth of impressive detail. And there is this to be said for it—that a man watching a football match tends to identify himself with the players: when one of them kicks a ball, his muscles twitch to do the same; when the goalkeeper leaps, he wants to leap. The absorbed identification of primitive man with the scene he was watching must have brought about just such reactions in him, yet if the circumstances compelled him for his safety to keep absolutely still, it is quite possible to argue that his reflexes found relief in mouth and tongue movements which would not betray him. Yet why need speech have been associated with them? Sound would give man away. There is no certainty that speech came this way: possibly the mouth and tongue and glottal gestures could have had no point until in fact the creature could already speak.

All these theories consider speech as arising from some interior need of a creature to utter sounds: they are egocentric theories. The only exception is the babble theory of the origin of language which considers language to begin not really with infantile babbling which merely exercises the vocal cords and provides the baby with its repertoire of sounds and noises, but with the act of the parent which bends over the child and interprets its sounds, and attaches meaning to them and encourages the child to use those which the parent 'understands'. Language then begins with *the discovery of communication*—that certain sounds carry certain meanings to listeners and produce always the same result.

Yet, all said and done, so much of this is speculation. The evidence in every field is slight, except perhaps for onomatopoeia. Many words are built up onomatopoeically, but many are not, and with those that are not, so unnatural are the sounds, so artificial, that a simple change of consonants, or reversal of them, produces an entirely different meaning. 'Dog' reversed becomes 'God'; 'not' reversed becomes 'ton'; 'meat' with a change of ending becomes 'mean' or 'mead', or 'meal', or, as far as sound goes, 'meek' or 'mere': changes of the first consonant produce 'feat', 'beat', 'wheat' and so forth, meanings all so different that the onomatopoeic theory breaks down completely. The examples given from the English tongue can be paralleled in any language. In short, the effort to find a source for language in natural sounds is a hopeless one, as hopeless as would be the task of finding an explanation of art in terms of the materials of the artist, or of proposing to discover the nature of literature in paper and ink. True, one can say that certain media are more suitable than others for arts, but that in no manner explains *what* man does with them, for art is not made of them, only through them. In the same way, the fact that language is made out of sound simply indicates that sound is a suitable medium, the natural sounds of men and the animals being no more than the raw material from which speech is made. But other media were available, and have been used—hand and body gesture, facial expression, the deaf and dumb alphabet and so on. Nor have the first two ever been abandoned as a means of communication. They enjoy their own vigorous and revealing life, as those who have visited 'The Family of Man' photographic exhibition must realize. In some things they are superior to speech. A facial expression exceeds in subtlety anything that can be said in words—try to describe the *expression* of a woman in love in words and one soon comes to recognize the hopeless inadequacy of even highly flexible languages for so many human purposes, and baffled, one abandons the task. But facial expressions have never developed into a language even as formal as gesture language. It has been said that spoken language is simply the survivor (by a process of natural selection) of several kinds of language, including particularly gesture. This would be more acceptable if spoken language in fact did more adequately what gesture and expression also do. But the spheres are just not the same: the eloquent shrug of an outraged or bored man is not something which can be conveyed so immediately, forcefully or subtly by speech. To put into words the wry expression of a child who has tasted a bitter substance would take tedious sentences. Gesture and expression are eloquent means of conveying feelings, emotions and subjective states, and perhaps are all the better for being left unformalized, for then the opportunities for insincerity and deception are fewer. But they do not do the work of speech, nor could ever do it. Speech, albeit clumsily and slowly, does what neither of the other two do, and is therefore not a competitor for survival with gesture and expression, any more than sculpture is a competitor with painting and embroidery. It will I hope become clear as we proceed just what speech could do that other forms of language could not.

The American Professor, William Dwight Whitney, a contemporary of Darwin (and a better and more conscientious linguist) produced in *Language and the Study of Language* (1868) a far more thorough study of linguistic problems than anything Darwin had to say. His book is a neglected masterpiece. In it he sought to show how, in relation to the Indo-European language, it was possible to pare away words in common use until one came to an irreducible root. One example he uses is *irrevocability*. The prefixes and suffixes can all be pared away. They can be shown to be other words, or parts of other words, introduced to modify or qualify the original root. There are many examples —*re*voke, *in*voke, *e*voke—of prefixes, and similarly of suffixes. But *voke* (Lat. vocare: to call) is the root. 'But while, in our own language, *voke* appears as a simple syllable, uncombined with suffixes, this is only by the comparatively recent effect of the wearing-out processes . . . in the more original Latin, it is invariably associated with formative elements, which compose with its forms like *vocare*, "to call", *vocat*, "he calls", *vocabar*, "I was called", or, in substantive uses, *vocs(vox)*, "a calling, a voice", *vocum*, "of voices", and so on. There is nothing, so far as concerns the formative elements themselves, to distinguish this last class of cases from the other, before analysed; each suffix has a distinct meaning and office, and is applied to a whole class of analogous words; and some of them, at least, are traceable back to the independent words out of which they grew. The only difference is that here, if we cut off the formative elements, we have left, not a word, actually employed as such in any ancient language of our family, but a significant syllable, expressing the general and indeterminate idea of "calling", and found to occur in connected speech only when limited and defined by the suffixes which are attached to it. This is not, however, a peculiarity which can exempt the words so formed from a like treatment, leading to like conclusions, with the rest; we must still trust in the reality of our analysis; and especially, when we consider such forms as the Sanskrit *vak-mi*, *vak-shi*, *vak-ti*, where the *mi*, *shi* and *ti* are recognizable pronouns, making compounds which mean clearly, "call-I", "call-thou", "call-he", we cannot doubt that the element *voc* (*vak*) had also once an independent status, that it was a word, a part of spoken speech, and that the various forms which it contains were really produced by the addition of other elements to it, and their fusion together in a single word, in the same manner in which we have fused *truth* and *full* into *truthful*, *truth* and *loose* into *truthless*. . .'[1]

And he goes on, significantly, 'The conclusion is one of no small consequence. Elements like *voc*, each composing a single syllable, and containing no traceable sign of a formative element, resisting all attempts at reduction to a simpler form, are what we arrive at as the final results of our analysis of the Indo-European vocabulary; every word of which this is made up— save those whose history is obscure . . . is found to contain a monosyllabic root as its central significant portion. . .'[2] And so

[1] *Language and the Study of Language*, pp. 254-5.
[2] Ibid., pp. 254 et seq.

he comes to the conclusion that the roots of our family of languages are divided into two classes—those which indicate position merely, and those which indicate some significant action or quality: into, in fact, demonstrative or pronominal roots, and predicative or verbal roots. In the pronominal roots he discovers a limited number of monosyllables, hardly more than a dozen, in which the letter *m* is usually used to indicate the subject, *t* and *n* more demonstratively, and *k* interrogatively. Instances he quotes are *ma, na, tu, ka*. The roots of the verbal sort are far more complicated in number and form. He gives such instances as *i* and *ga* and *ak*, denoting forms of motion, *stā* for standing, *ās* and *sad* for sitting, *sarp* for creeping, *pat* for flying, and so forth. His examples are illuminating.

One can visualize, indeed, the possibility that speech developed in this way, and moreover it would have become infinitely complicated almost on the instant of invention. *Ma, na, tu* at least are forms of naming. They point at a person or a thing. But if once they become added to the verbal roots, then names are upon us with the rapidity of hailstones in a storm. It is only necessary to add the pronoun to the verbal root to get something more than the declension of a verb. If one speaks constantly of 'burns-it', 'creeps-it', 'flies-it' (or 'it-burns', 'it-creeps', etc.) then we need not doubt that presently a permanent word form is set up which becomes the noun—*fire, serpent, bird*. But this too is speculation, for the truth remains that the roots which Professor Whitney exposed, and which the temptation is to regard as simple, could still be the worn stumps of what were originally very complicated verbal processes. All that we can learn from Professor Whitney's work is how spoken language *might* have grown from very simple speech origins.

If we look at the languages of the world today, though we find great variations between them in subtlety, complexity and scope, we do not find a rudimentary or primitive language from which it is possible that other languages evolved or developed. We find poor languages and rich languages, but the poverty and richness are directly related to the cultural life of the peoples who speak them. 'A language fits a culture as the skin fits a snake,' Professor Coon remarked. 'A language is a mirror image of a culture.' For this reason not all ideas are equally expressible in different languages, but most ideas can come to be expressed in most living languages, though the effort may involve laborious circumlocutions. If this were not so, I am afraid that the flourishing British and Foreign Bible Society would long ago have gone out of existence. Some languages have no words for vital ideas or experiences which others are able to express with ease. Yet this does not necessarily involve us in labelling some advanced and others primitive in an evolutionary sense. It is again a consequence of what is experienced, or regarded as significant in experience, in the context of a particular culture. And languages, in any case, have always been ready to borrow from each other to cover deficiencies in vocabulary.

It is clear that language is a human art which has to be learnt, not evolved into. Wild children brought up by bears and wolves learn no language. If left too long without human company, they reach the stage at which they never learn—their vocal organs have lost their flexibility and the cerebral tramlines remain unlaid. But in human company they will learn one language as readily as another. Bring up an aborigine in England and it will learn English as its mother tongue and speak it with a facility probably equal to that of anyone with an English inheritance: bring up a white child in an aboriginal camp and the same process will hold good. 'All speech is one,' Professor Whitney wrote in the 11th Edition of the *Encyclopaedia Britannica*, 'in the sense that every human being, of whatever race he may be, is capable of acquiring any existing tongue and of using it for the same purposes for which its present possessors use it, with such power and effect as his individual capacity allows, and without any essential change in the mental operations carried on by speech . . .' Has anyone ever questioned that statement? It reveals, more surely than anything else, speech as the common condition of humanity.

As I have tried to show, we do not know anything about the speech of the earliest men. That there were speech forms older than even the most primitive to-day we can be sure, for Australian aborigines and Amazonian Guaharibos have a language which they use in ceremonial ways of which they themselves understand not a word—as if Christians were still to use a Latin liturgy though all memory of the meaning of Latin had disappeared. But even such archaic aboriginal words as survive do not suggest in their form, when written down, a language less complex than that possessed by the aborigines to-day.

Father Jacob Baegert, who wrote about the extinct Californian Indians nearly two hundred years ago, had this to say about the language of these backward and primitive people: 'The Waïcuri language is of an exceedingly barbarous and rude description, by which rudeness, however, I do not mean a hard pronunciation or a succession of many consonants, for these qualities do not form the essence of a language, but merely its outward character and conformation . . . but the great deficiency of language consists in the total absence of a great many words, the want of which would seem to render it almost impossible for reasonable beings to converse with each other and to receive instruction in the Christian religion. For whatever is not substantial, and cannot be seen or touched or otherwise perceived by the senses, has no name in the Waïcuri language. There are no nouns whatever for expressing virtues, vices, or the different dispositions of the mind, and there exist only a few adjectives of this class, namely, *merry, sad, lazy* and *angry*, all of which merely denote such humours as can be perceived in a person's face. All terms relating to rational human and civil life, and a multitude of words for signifying other objects, are entirely wanting, so that it would be a vain trouble to look in the Waïcuri vocabulary for the following expressions: *life, death, weather, time, cold, heat, world, rain, understanding, will, memory, knowledge, honour*—' Father Baegert's list is a long one, and I will not quote the whole of it—'the word *living* they have neither as a noun nor as a verb, neither in a natural nor a moral sense: but only the adjective *alive. Bad, narrow, short, distant, little*, etc., they cannot express unless by adding the negation *ja* or *ra* to the words *good, wide, long, near*, and *much*. They have particular words for signifying *an old man, an old woman, a young man, a young woman*, and so

L   161

forth; but the terms *old* or *young* do not exist in their language. . .'[1]

Father Baegert himself sees the problem of Waïcuri language
in its proper setting when he explains that so many terms necessary to us are missing from the Waïcuri vocabulary because
those who speak the language have no use for such terms; 'their
almost animal-like existence and narrow compass of ideas rendering the application of such expressions superfluous'. Yet his
general critical attack stems from his own European background
with its linguistic knowledge and background, and rich culture
and written tongues. And it seems to me that there is all the
difference in the world between a language which can check itself by resort to a written form and an agreed grammar, and one
which cannot. To the Western mind what we say is as it were a
reading of what somewhere is previously written. The language
we speak has visual resources. No such rich second layer is
available to the language which is only spoken, nor I would
suggest is the method of the Western grammarian adequate for
dealing with it. Context must be everything in primitive speech
and the one thing which cannot be written down phonetically
is context. 'Communication,' wrote William J. Entwistle, in
Aspects of Language, 'lies partly in what we say, partly in circumstances. The latter fill in so much that actual speaking is elliptical, erratic, incomplete, and imprecise. Even the elliptical
words may be further curtailed by substituting gestures, which
refer one back vaguely to the circumstances. Thus one may
overhear:

> *A.* Hullo! How's tricks?
> *B.* So so; and the boy?
> *A.* Bursting with energy, thanks.'[2]

One might multiply such conversations from observation in
any saloon bar in any public house in London and an analysis

---

[1] *Account of the Aboriginal Inhabitants of the Californian Peninsula:* in the
Reports of the Smithsonian Institute 1863 and 1864. From C. S. Coon, *A
Reader in General Anthropology*, p. 81.

[2] Op. cit., London, 1953, p. 11. *See also* the conversation on p. 12 of the
same work.

of them would show that sustained conversations are carried on in phrases which lack 'subject, object, verb, and other principal parts'! In order to understand the difficulties facing the ethnologist or anthropologist—(and Professor Evans-Pritchard gives an account of them in his book *The Nuer*)—we ought to imagine what would confront a Martian anthropologist compiling a grammar and vocabulary of the English language from just such saloon-bar conversations transcribed phonetically. He might well conclude that it was poverty-stricken and lacking in form.

The aboriginal Arunta People of Northern Australia speak a language deficient in many of the elements we should consider necessary. 'The Arunta do not differentiate vowels or distinguish between voiced and voiceless consonants, nor do they insist on the precise limits of syllables. . . They use no gender. Their basic stems are gerundial, i.e. indifferently nominal or verbal, and as they usually form parts of agglomerations, they seem unfinished in themselves. There is no definite subordination of suffixes to principal stems. The suffixes are also principal stems in their own right, and the union of stems and suffixes seems to be temporary. This is so unlike agglutination in the Turkish fashion (which depends on a strict differentiation of principal stems and relational suffixes) that it should not be called by the same name but by some other, such as agglomeration.'[1]

Yet of the Arunta language, Spencer and Gillen have said this in their classic work on these Stone Age people: 'The vocabulary is rich in terms denoting everything in their environment. Every animal and plant has its own name, each species, except the very small and insignificant ones, being recognized. Every feature in the landscape has its special name. . . In many respects their memory is phenomenal. Their mental powers are simply devoted along the lines which are of service to them in their daily life.'[2] In addition to this richness of vocabulary, the Arunta are said to possess a gesture language of at least 250

[1] Ibid., p. 163.
[2] Spencer and Gillen, *The Arunta*, London, 1927, vol. I, pp. 22-3.

signs. If then the form is primitive or undeveloped, if there are what Entwistle calls 'undifferentiated masses of pre-grammar' in the Arunta speech, yet this need not disqualify it from communications of the utmost subtlety within the terms of their own culture, such as the telling of their myths and the presentation of their endless and socially and cosmically significant ceremonies, such as the Intichiuma ceremonies of the sort already described. It is said that an Arunta, shown his own photograph, recognized in it not only himself, but also his brother and his totemic animal, and it is concluded that his life was entirely that of his clan and that he had no notion of 'Self'. This is to argue beyond the evidence, however. Effigies are familiar to us, but not necessarily to primitive peoples. And the Arunta's effigy was *not* himself, after all. One must allow for a certain primitive logic which says that *it is impossible* that an effigy of me should *be* me.

What I am hoping to show by these examples drawn from various authorities is the danger of writing down the stature of man of simpler cultures by a comparison, however oblique, with the speech forms of civilized man. The exercise involves numerous pitfalls and can lead to misunderstandings comparable with those which the Darwinian effort to fix man in the frame of nature gave rise to. Professor Carleton Coon is close to the point when he speaks of language fitting a culture as a skin fits a snake. It is a mirror-image of a culture, he wrote. That too is open to misunderstanding, as though the material environment and social organization called forth a language to fit it. Yet the truth lies deeper: it is that possession of a language permitted the creation of a culture up to the limit of physical means. The environment puts limits to what the culture can be or can do: it does not put the culture there in the first place.

Even a clumsy and primitive language represents an incredible advance on the ten or so recorded calls of the gibbon, and how the conquest of speech really was made, in the end we do not know. We can only wonder at the fact that the most difficult of all human inventions was the first. If man had come to speech as the crown of a long struggle with himself and the forces of nature, that would have been easier to understand than the high probability that in the most primitive societies men already spoke to each other not only about *meat, sleep, fire, enemies,* and *sexual intercourse,* but about *love* and *hate,* and *good* and *bad,* the *visible* and the *invisible,* the *secular* and the *sacred.* It seems improbable that subman reached the stature of man except in society: it seems unlikely that society could have had the revolutionary effect thus predicated of it, without *language.* Which came first—man, or society, or language? One has really to postulate the simultaneous arrival of all three in one of those phases of explosive evolution the prehistorians talk about.

III

However, there is no way of grasping the full significance of language by asking only about its origins, as though one had only to explain the origin of a thing to have it explained away. The evolutionary thesis has so obsessed us with the search for origins that we are incapable of looking beyond them, though in a score of matters origins explain less than functions. The origin of a violin in the twanging of a bow string does not really explain the violin. The steam engine 'originated' in the boiling tea kettle, but that does not explain what a steam engine is, what it does, or why it was invented. We can only understand the significance of speech in the human situation by asking what it does. To this I must now turn.

Speech is the organization of sound, which is the most evanescent and immaterial of the phenomena which go to make up our material universe. It is, because of its evanescence and immateriality, the least *organized* (normally) of the forms with which we are surrounded in our daily life. We cannot catch a sound and preserve it: we cannot wing it in its flight and bring it to earth.[1] This is the fleeting material which man has captured for speech. Though man's body produces sounds—his

---

[1] At least man could not until this century. Recording devices now accomplish even this.

feet pad the earth, or brush through grass, his breathing makes a noise, his heart thumps, and he lets off cries and ejaculations—speech makes use only of the sounds which man produces with his vocal cords. But the natural sounds those cords make (like the strange animal cries deaf and dumb children produce in their excitement, and which, of course, they cannot hear) are inarticulate: they will go on as long as the man feels urged to make them, or breath lasts. In this capacity man is like the animals which produce cries or calls with several meanings (as again deaf and dumb children do) because different states of excitement produce a different tension in the vocal cords and a higher or lower speed in the expulsion of breath. However, though the cries are differentiated from each other by their meaning, the sounds which make up one natural cry are undifferentiated: they are almost like Professor Whitney's roots, they cannot reduce themselves any further.

Now man has worked both deliberately and unconsciously on the raw material his vocal cords will produce and fashioned a highly artificial and synthetic accomplishment. What is the nearest parallel to it? Perhaps the contortionist: the trainer of contortionists will take a child when its limbs and bones and muscles are still plastic and still growing and train it to contort those limbs, and indeed its whole body, until the child is capable of wrapping its feet around its own neck and putting its body into a number of highly stylised and quite unnatural physical positions. In the same way, the speech of man has been created by a systematic stylisation of natural sounds, as Professor Higgins was most determined to explain to Liza Doolittle in Shaw's *Pygmalion*.

First of all, in speech, the natural continuity of sound which may depend solely on breathing and the irrationality of the breaks in it, is abandoned. The sound is chopped into definite lengths—an arbitrary proceeding and one which (if the speech of the Arunta People is a precedent) may have been mastered with difficulty. Man is capable of making (broadly) two kinds of sounds, which we call vowels and consonants: the vowel is the result of shaping his mouth and letting an uninterrupted sound

166

of one sustained tone come out. The articulation of a consonant involves on the other hand a marked muscular movement in one or more parts of the mouth to force out a hard or violent sound, *p, b, t, d, k, g* etc. The vowel is a sound which could become aimless, but the powerful consonant is used to control it— to open up a vowel sound as in *too*, or to close it as in *at*, or to enclose the sound completely with intensity and emphasis, as in *dog*. The value of the consonantal control is immense: not only do the consonants enable vowels to be introduced and then cleared out of the way immediately they have had their effect: the *duration* of a sound is thereby controlled, and this is an important aspect of speech: the essence of the process of articulation is the artificial limitation of the duration of sounds: a child with a speech defect which prevents it from sounding its consonants has particular difficulty in bringing them to an end once it has embarked on them. They trail off, but in trailing off, lose their clarity. The defective child's sounds become like the noises Eliza Doolittle made.

Speech, then, becomes the ability to reproduce in an infinite variety of ways and in endless combinations the open and closed sounds of the voice in conjunction with those sometimes almost imperceptible silences which mark the point of disjunction between one group of sounds and another. Let it be said that this is a highly difficult physical process in its own right, as the singer knows, as the student discovers when he has to learn the consonantal and vowel values of a strange language, even though he is predisposed to the artifice of the whole proceeding by what he has learnt of his own language. But language would be nothing but an interesting experiment in voice organization if it remained that. It is the intellectual use of this device which is so extraordinary, *and this is even more artificial*. Every artificially contrived sound which man makes in this way is associated with a particular object or activity or concept of his total experience. More, the sounds he ejects are organized to render an account of the position and movements of objects in time and space. It is a process of the intellectualization of his world, for his language comes to agree with what he decides is the articu-

lated structure of his world itself. Leaving aside for the moment
some of the refinements of language, we can say that every
sound in some way *belongs* to an object—by convention, of
course, but that is the same as saying 'by a creative act'—and
presently belongs with such an inherent right or automatic
association that for the speaking man it is difficult to dissociate
the word from the object or experience.

Languages grow. They change and develop, shed old words
and old meanings and acquire new, as experiences change or
knowledge accumulates; pronunciations alter and (for written
languages) spellings change. The mutability of language caused
Darwin to formulate his theory of the natural selection of words
and languages. Sometimes the changes can be observed by
living people—most easily by those of us who have lived since
the invention of printing. But though the change is real, it is
very slow even among people with written and printed languages who can more easily absorb new speech forms into the living tongue. Among primitive peoples we may hazard a guess
that it is exceedingly slow, yet real nevertheless or we should not
have records of aboriginal 'Latin'. Yet for all the change, the
most interesting aspect of language is the permanence of association between sound and thing through hundreds of generations. The capricious sound has been married to an iron discipline. The *cat*, once so named, remains a cat to the people of
that language. Man easily tires, he is always looking for the new
thing; he is endlessly resourceful about his crafts and techniques.
The tool of yesterday no longer satisfies him to-day: the crude
stone knife so laboriously fashioned is abandoned for the
polished one, the stone one for a bronze, the bronze for an iron,
and so forth. The tool is transformed beyond all recognition;
and yet it is conceivable that throughout all such changes its
name will remain the same.[1] Language is in this sense the most
conservative of inventions, and that man should have restrained
private or public caprice or fashion in this field of enterprise is
really quite remarkable. That most impermanent thing, sound,

[1] We still call a certain leather or wooden chest *a trunk*, for originally it
was the hollowed-out trunk of a tree.

when arbitrarily organized, becomes permanently associated with the thing or activity to which man has decided to allot it. A miracle! a *necessary* miracle too, for a sound is a symbol which can be transported with no effort, which never gets too heavy to carry, which can be reproduced at will in its original form and retains always that form apart from such accidents it suffers through the vagaries of memory. It is less perishable therefore than more apparently durable things, and can be reproduced and broadcast and made common property simply because of the ease of its manufacture. It has in its very lack of attachment and lack of concreteness an affinity to the spirit which it must serve. There is therefore through the invention of speech the entry into and exploration of a new dimension of human activity. I think it was rather provincial and dull-witted of Darwin not to have shown a glimmer of interest in all this.

So much for what language is in the technical sense.

Let us now look at what it does.

A savage comes down to a water hole at evening to drink and is surprised and scared off by a lion. That, since lions are familiar if fearsome objects, is the end of the thing. He goes on with his affairs. The next evening, at the same time, he sees a small boy going down to the same water hole to drink. He says to him: 'You should not go there. Yesterday I was there and a lion nearly got me.' And so the boy listens, and understands, and goes home to drink from his mother's waterpot.

Let us contrast this with another, and as common, and as natural an event.

A thrush has her nest in the fork of a tree in the garden of a private house. She lays her eggs and sits to hatch off her brood. One day the tree is shaken and a boy's head appears. She squawks and flies away. The boy counts the clutch and goes down the tree and retreats indoors. The thrush, observing the retreat of the enemy, goes back to her nest, and settles down. Presently the cock bird returns, he observes nothing except that the hen is perhaps still in a slight state of alarm. Her state of alarm could be (*a*) hawk, (*b*) rat, (*c*) boy, (*d*) bird neighbours, (*e*) cold, (*d*) hunger or thirst, but as the cock bird neither sees nor is affected himself by any of these contingencies, the anxiety of his mate conveys no meaning to him. He is unable to take any action, because he does not know of any cause so to do. The next evening, the boy, having fallen to temptation, climbs up the tree again and takes two eggs of the clutch. The hen has been driven away, and she returns to find two eggs gone: or at least, she suspects that eggs are gone because the configuration is different and there is the smell of the boy's hand in the nest. But she cannot count and goes on sitting, rather more disturbed. The cock bird returns. He may observe the distress, and come to discover that eggs are missing, perhaps even by a note in the bird's greeting. But again he has no means of knowing what the cause was, and therefore cannot remedy it or take preventive action. The night following two boys appear. The small boy has boasted of his haul, and now others want a share. The nest is cleared. The cock bird returns to find this, and the nest is abandoned. The pair go to the end of the garden and there build again, where again the same process is repeated for the birds have not built out of reach of the small boy.

This is a situation which calls out for language. Had there been even the rudiments of language, of communication of experience, then at least the mistake of building again where a boy was likely to climb would not have been repeated.

In the case of the native and the boy and the lion, the human mastery of the situation is almost complete. Speech would have enabled an interchange:

Boy: Does the lion only come down at evening?
Man: Yes.
Boy: Then I will go to drink at the high noon.
or
Boy: Is there a lion there now?
Man: I do not think so.
Boy: Then watch for me while I drink, for I am very thirsty.
or
Boy: Has the lion killed many people?
Man: Yes.
Boy: Perhaps we had better change our water hole.

Man: Perhaps we had better kill the lion.

And so on—for the possibility of intercourse is endless. Let us give it all to the thrushes.

Hen: A boy climbed up and drove me off.

Cock: When was this?

Hen: An hour ago.

Cock: Then tomorrow I stay around and peck him if he tries again.

or, when two eggs had been taken:

Cock: Perhaps it is useless to stay. We must build again.

Hen: We must build out of reach, or he will climb there too.

If the thrushes had adapted some of their beautiful modulations of voice to these purposes, then we can see that such attacks would have resulted in the complete modification of their life-pattern to meet such emergencies—surely a capacity with an important survival value? And the thrush cannot be indifferent to the value of sound, since the songs it sings are designed to warn intruders off its territory, or to attract a mate, or to express its *joie de vivre*. It is quick to take up the song challenge of a rival. Some key factor is missing in the thrush situation and this must rule out language. If we examine again the speech elements in the dialogue between the native and the boy we may discover what they are.

The really important information conveyed by the man to the boy is contained in the second sentence spoken in the imaginary encounter:

Yesterday I was there and a lion nearly got me.

There stands for the place, which might be emphatically pointed out by the hand also, or with a gesture of the head. What has to be associated with *place* is *a lion*. But there is no lion present and visible, or even suspected. The object to which the boy's attention is being drawn must be placed not simply in space, but in time also. Instead of saying 'Lion—there!' as the man would have done had the lion actually been there in that indicated place, the narrator has to introduce the element of time: without it his story would be untrue. And so he says, '*Yesterday*, I *was* there and a lion nearly *got* me.' The three italicized words place the event firmly in the absolute past, which is quite dissociated grammatically from the immediate present. These words, with the adverb *nearly*, explain why it is that the lion is not there, but was there, and why the man is alive and uninjured. But the whole story about the past now justifies the warning about *the future* contained in the first sentence.

'You should not go there.' The conditional however describes a condition of freedom about the future. What is said is not 'You will not go there' or 'You cannot go there' but you *should* not, meaning you can go there if you like but it would be wiser not to.

Perhaps all the elements of mental activity which make speech essential to man are in these simple sentences. They are:

1. Clear memories of the past.
2. Capacity to associate those memories with the present situation.
3. Ability to foresee a future situation in the light of both.
4. Power to decide what to do about that future situation in the light of more than one possibility.

It is these which are absent from the thrush situation and would make language useless to it, or nearly so, without an expansion of its capacity for understanding. It is doubtful whether the thrush remembers not just the event of the day before, but even the quite recent event: despite bird capacity to learn, which in a limited way certainly exists, the danger past is the danger forgotten as the cloud past is the cloud forgotten. This absence of a body of memories which can be manipulated in the mind of a thrush is perhaps the most important deficiency of all: without it the others cannot be born. For though, for example, the thrush will recognize a danger, perhaps even a danger only once experienced, its instinct will simply be every time to flee. It will not be able to recall all the previous factors associated with that danger in order now to circumvent it. Nor will it, lacking a body of distinct memories, well-shaped, coherent and discrete, be able to foresee a future situation in which the separate elements of past experience may reassemble in an old or in a different pattern—still less to consider the various ways in which it might be met. Because it has no past which can be manipulated in the mind, it cannot consider how the future can be manipulated, and its freedom is therefore gravely restricted.

Now it is not speech which gives man these particular powers, though through speech he can make them clearer, sharper, and more easy to cope with. But it is speech which enables him to fix the transient and changing in such a pattern that the permanent can be distinguished from the impermanent, and securely registered and recalled by a word. And to this aspect of speech belongs man's power to name. Man is able to name because he is able to demarcate one object from another—to mark the grass from the tree, the tree from the sky, the squirrel from the tree, the woman from the waterpot, the gazelle from the river, and so forth. This power of clear demarcation in the mind gives his naming point: naming itself increases the power of demarcation by accustoming man from the cradle to mark one object off from another, and to register what is essential and what is accidental to the identification made, by words which conform to mental and visual imagery. Man is presented, as an animal or bird is presented, with an unbroken continuity of sensual experience of every kind in which it is difficult at first to distinguish the external from the internal experience. It seems that the animal only chooses to mark off distinctly from that continuum what comes to have special importance to it—danger, food, sex, shelter and so on—and, despite considerable animal curiosity, to ignore the rest, and even in the realms mentioned never to go far enough. But man demarcates everything. Man intellectualizes everything. One is saying by this either that he is curious about everything, which is certainly true, or what is more important that everything affects him, or that he influences everything or perhaps all three. Any or all of those capacities casts him for a most extraordinary rôle in the universe. It is hard to imagine anything farther from the instinctive, un-articulated cries of animals and birds than conventional language, in which sound is handled in a most arbitrary fashion, and fleeting combinations of sounds are enduringly related to solid objects out in the space that surrounds man.

'Soon', J. B. Watson wrote, 'the human has a verbal substitute within himself theoretically for every object in the world. Thereafter he carries the world around with him by means of this organization. And he can manipulate this world in the privacy of his room or when he lies down on his bed in the dark.'[1]

Man not only names the parts of the sensual continuum he can differentiate one from another, he names himself, and this self-naming is at least as important a function of speech as any other. Man has a word for himself, and this enables him to discover things about himself which otherwise might escape the understanding. It is the real beginning of the *subject-predicate* form of grammar to which the modern philosopher is apt to take such violent and quite unjustified exception, as though the discovery of it were the beginning of all falsity in the world of thought, whereas the opposite is true, that it was the beginning of the discovery of truth. Man chose to speak of himself as 'I', and by 'I' he did not mean the name of one more object in outer space, but of the subject, himself, which he discovers in 'inner space'. 'I' is the name which he gives to that sense of continuing identity. About that identity he makes the most interesting discoveries, as that, for instance, it changes: that some years ago he was smaller, feebler, undeveloped, uncircumcised; that even a year or two back he had not yet taken a wife; that far back though his memories go, to some event in infancy, there they stop; beyond that he cannot reach, but he has been told that he was a spirit in the ancestral totem well, swimming around like a fish, waiting to find his mother. His mind can reach forward, on the basis of the experiences of others, to a time when he will die, for others have died, and the old get feebler and feebler, and death seems appropriate for them. And then— will his identity go? That seems improbable, for he, or at least that immaterial part of him of which he is aware in his inwardness and in his dreams, is the 'spirit' which will return to the ancestral totem and await reincarnation. In some such way the most primitive of men comes to think. Whether what he thinks is true or false is at the moment immaterial, what is important

---

[1] *Behaviourism*, 1930, p. 234.

is that he has discovered that the identity of a thing continues under its changing appearances, forms and accidents. I think it is clear that no language could ever have developed at all without this discovery. The world of primitive man is a kaleidoscope of change. The tree looks different in evening light from morning light; different with leaves shed from the beauty of blossom time; different with limbs lopped than when its limbs are whole. The stoat in winter coat might be a different animal from the stoat in summer dress. The woman in pregnancy is greatly changed. The boy is physically altered by circumcision. Is one face to face with the same continuing object in each case, or with a succession of objects? If with a succession of objects, then one is compelled to adopt an equal succession of nouns (or abandon the task altogether as hopeless) and such a need multiplies immediately the number of necessary nouns to infinity, and would have imposed upon primitive man a feat of memory obviously beyond him (as it would equally be beyond us). What is more, it would have forbidden all intellectual recognition: the changing but indefinable continuum would have been back with a vengeance.

Man decided, *on the analogy of his own inward experience*, that the continuum consisted of enduring things, of permanent identities, which were not destroyed in their identities by suffering a succession of accidents of form or appearance: that the word *stoat* would cover all the guises in which the stoat appeared from birth to death, and that the shifting variety of forms and circumstances in which it appeared could best be covered by the predication to it from time to time of changing qualities and activities. Thus one could describe the stoat as *sleeping*, without having to imply that it was permanently sleeping, or that it had ceased to be the same being as the stoat *running*. In the same measure 'sleeping' could be added to or taken away from the babe without any alteration of the baby's identity. Indeed, only by this or some similar organization of language was it possible to cope even inadequately with the infinite variety of activity in the changing world.

Now this particular task is imposed upon man by his sense of the passage of time. If there were *no* time factor involved (if such an absurdity is possible to imagine), then every object would be changeless and named once for all: it would never appear in any other guise except that of its instantaneous appearance, but the discovery which man makes of his own permanence of identity under a succession of changes is the discovery of time; with that discovery he begins to range across past time, and to look forward imaginatively into the future. He takes possession of time. And the principal problems of language range round the time factor: how to hold fast to the permanent identities and yet to account for their changing qualities in time. Place or space, in a sense, is a subsidiary problem, for there could be no changes of objects in space without the time in which to permit them to do so. And there is for him an identity between the time over which he himself can move in memory and the time through which all things move. For the time-span during which he himself has changed without loss of identity, is the time-span in which other things have changed without loss of identity.

In the second chapter I spoke of the difference between the natural cycle and human history: I spoke of the narrow band of light which represented the life of the animal fulfilling itself through the natural cycle, and the broader band of the life of man conscious not simply of the immediate present but of the generations before him and the generations to follow. When we lift the same man out of the natural cycle and put him in history, then we find that his range over time is potentially infinite: he can look backward across time as far as the evidence will take him, and forward into the future, at least into what he imagines the future will be, again, just so far as the evidence will allow him to go. In the process of discovering himself in time, and then ranging over it, man conquers time, as he conquers space, first by the carrying power of his voice, then by messages sent by runners, then by pieces of paper with marks on them, then by telegram, radio, television and all the modern miracles of communication. Man begins, with his mind, to transcend time and space, and speech is the point which marks the occurence. It is the invention of the ship to sail on the ocean of the spirit.

Professor R. A. Wilson has beautifully explored the space-time conquest which language represents in his *The Miraculous Birth of Language*,[1] in which he describes human language as an emergent which marks a new step forward in evolution on to a plane of activity and experience quite unpredictable from anything that we have learnt from animal behaviour. He says about it that 'language, then, is a new phenomenon in the world, brought to life at that point where the reason of the world emerges from its inconscious state to its freed and conscious life. There is always a difficulty in coming to a mutual understanding upon the connotation of words; but it becomes palpably clear when the subject is developed in this way that to call the natural cries of animals language, without some specific qualification of the word, is a sheer confusion of all significant differences in reality and thought. The animals, as yet at least, have no free space-time world of mind whose detailed elaboration necessitates the symbols which we call language, and until they have such a world they can have no language in any exact connotation of the word.'[2]

And again: 'Man's problem was to intellect the world; to translate the types from the world of nature to the world of mind, and in this way elaborate the world of mind. It is the generation and evolution of a new world. This generation is a time process, and sound as a time expression was the direct and natural medium by means of which the generating process could be actualized. By articulation and conventionalization man succeeded in making sounds express objects in space as well as sequence in time, and in this way transmuted sound into an adequate single vehicle for representing a space-time world.'[3]

Yet in a way the discussion of language in Professor Wilson's excellent book could still make language a private and personal possession: a means, in that quotation from Watson which he too uses, of private manipulation within one's skull of the outer space-time world. True language does serve that function, but man *by himself* would neither invent language nor need it: man

[1] 1937, under the title of *The Birth of Language*.
[2] Ibid., 1942 Edn., p. 152.   [3] Ibid., p. 172.

invents, or discovers, or has born in him the powers of speech because of his need of communication within a society of his peers. As well as the *ego* as the source of speech, there is what Professor Entwistle called the *tu*. Language is for man above all the means of communicating his experiences and states of mind to others of his kind, and of rousing in them the capacity to share what has happened physically, socially, spiritually to him. Without the listening ears, there is no language, but only cries in the dark. The problems of language lead straight therefore to the meaning of *communication* in human history.

CHAPTER 8

The Lord and Giver of Life

In stepping out of nature, into history, man makes himself free of the dimension of time. It hardly needs saying that time is of the essence of vitality. The life of an organism is irreversible: once given its lease of life it must run through its time and die. But all that it is possessed of is its own stretch of time. Its band of awareness does not permit it experience or understanding of that which lies beyond the band. What is outside its own time band is outside its experience.[1] In a similar way, an organism is circumscribed in space: its body is extended in space, and it possesses or conquers a certain area of space, the prisoner's 'little tent of sky', and moves within it, and knows little or nothing of space beyond, incapable of the concepts of infinite space or curved space of the human mind, or of investigating them. The space and time which are the grace by which an organism lives also hold it in thrall. It is their prisoner and does not know by what it is imprisoned. So that to speak of man as making himself free of time can only mean that he achieves

---

[1] I have to ignore, indeed to dismiss, theories of the Eternal Present which by stressing that all experienced events, including experience of the past, take place in the present, contrive to make the past, and time itself, unreal. This seems to me essentially the solipsistic fallacy, in one of its many mystic disguises, that everything which is not present does not exist. If it should turn out that the theory of the Eternal Present was true, we should have to face a still greater difficulty—how to account for the *illusion* of time, the *illusion* of a past. I have dealt with problems of time in 'Nature and Time'—Chap. 1 of *The Meaning of Human Existence*.

a certain limited independence of it without destruction of his organic status. He transcends time in some manner. He is able to range backwards and forwards along the time dimension: this is what we mean by acts of memory, or foresight, and provision for the future. Yet by such activities he imaginatively reconstructs his world, which is as much as to say that he manipulates time, as perhaps a hunting animal manipulates the space in which it lives when it beats an area or runs to cut off its prey, and it is possible that such manipulation could take place without any special consciousness of what was being manipulated. But man not only manipulates space and time, he stands sufficiently above or apart from them to understand *what* it is he is manipulating. He knows there is such a thing as time, and such a thing as space, and understands and comes to terms with the conditions they impose on his life and knowledge. He knows (for the most part intuitively, of course) that he cannot break the conditions in any physical or material sense. He cannot return with his body to a past time, any more than he can translate himself across space without movement through it. Nor can he project himself as an organism into a future he believes to be coming, however desirable. So that his acts of transcension are in no sense material or vital ones. If they exist they must be of another kind, or take place in another 'dimension'. They must be acts of projection of the same kind as those which enable a man to enter into the sufferings or joys of another, to understand and to be moved by the message of great works of art or of music. They must be projections such as those which enabled the Paleolithic hunter to identify himself with his fleet-footed prey. We have no other word than *spirit* to describe this unique human endowment. 'It is roughly the same thing as feeling or thought,' Santayana wrote in almost the same connection, 'it might be indentified as the *pensée* or cogitatio of Descartes or Spinoza.'[1] More to the point, Santayana argued that spirit was that which was immune from the material flux of existence. Like A. N. Whitehead, he thought of spirit as saving what was valuable in the wreckage of temporal change, and carrying it forward to

[1] *The Realm of Spirit*, London, 1940, p. vii.

immortality. Spirit distinguishes precisely those primitive forms of human activity which this book has made an effort to isolate and analyse in order that the distinctly human might be contrasted with that which is below it in nature. Perhaps most characteristic of the human is that ability, which language shows man to possess, to extract himself from his animal being and contemplate the world in which he is caught *sub specie aeternitatis*. When man looks at himself and his world intellectually, morally, and aesthetically, when he seeks to understand, to judge, to order, and to create, he is living in the dimension of the spiritual which, in the end, since it is flame, needs burning words to describe it. 'This inner light is indeed requisite for focusing impressions and rendering them mentally present, but it is biologically prior to them, vital and central, a product of combustion, a leaping flame, a fountain and seat of judgment. I therefore call it spirit; not that I think it either a substance or a physical power, or capable of existing by itself, but that it is a personal and moral focus of life, where the perspectives of nature are reversed as in a mirror and attached to the fortunes of a single soul.'[1]

I think it is more easy to understand what is involved in this new dimension of spirit which man explores if we look back again at the realm of the animal. Derek Wragge Morley in his study, *The Ant World*,[2] has painted a fascinating picture of the genius and enterprise of the ants in the building of communities, and in their colonizing, food-hoarding and growing, and 'cattle-rearing' activities. We learn that every ant community contains some individuals who are more than usually quick and energetic. They are the 'job-starters' who wake more rapidly than others to the needs of a situation; collectively they constitute a kind of excitement centre which galvanizes the whole ant community into the necessary activity by which it survives, grows, and spreads. When the first signs of spring come and the sunlight penetrates the dome of the nest, this, or hunger, wakes some ants from their fast sleep in the warm nest down below. Workers come out in search of food, 'and the first to set to work

---

[1] Ibid., p. 8.   [2] London, 1953.

are the job-starters—those inevitable individuals, the excitement centres. In the early days even they remain near the nest, their movements are less elastic and their contacts with other ants less animated and their stimulation consequently less viable.'[1] But presently the whole ant-heap is busy, and soon the immediate vicinity is cleared of accumulated food and 'trails are pushed outwards. Already the pattern of memory is being jogged. Each journey outwards re-establishes another link in the chain which will eventually build the whole. It is a slow process by human standards, this progressive awakening of the ant mind to memories of the previous year. Yet it is an individual process dependent on the minute grey cells found even within the humble brain of the ant.'[2] As memories re-awaken, so the nest re-establishes the old pattern of tracks to its food resources, makes contact along the fringes of its trail with its own colonies, and rediscovers its frontiers against both friends and foes. What seems to determine policy in the ant-heap is a collective and highly communicable excitement which perhaps stems in the first place from the job-starters. 'The emotive forces flow outward from each individual to his neighbours and in the opposite direction at varying *tempi*. When excitement develops, each individual receives impulses at a greater rate and of greater intensity from all the surrounding individuals, and since they are being excited, moving rapidly to and fro, from more of them. As its own excitement mounts as the result of this vast inflow of tensions, so its own impulses flow outward at an ever-increasing rate, and its own more and more hurried movements bring it into contact with more and more individuals from whom and to whom it both receives and gives ever more intense and frequent stimuli. . .'[3]

Through the excitement communicated physically by the ants one to another, the entire community is geared up in the event of trouble, but very obviously at enormous expenditures of energy in aimless rushing to and fro to find the 'something to

[1] *The Ant World*, 1953, p. 73. The account is of the activities of the *Formicas*.
[2] Ibid., p. 73.　　　　　　[3] Ibid., p. 171.

do'—fight, swarm, or migrate—at which the excitement points. The excitement can even be fatal, Mr. Wragge Morley tells us. An ant in pain, and with its sense of smell destroyed, can start off 'a hundred battles to the death'. It goes berserk, and strikes anywhere, until in the end the community is destroying itself in wanton and aimless internecine warfare. So indeed an anthill can be wiped out by sprinkling sublimate over a few of its members.

Among the ants we divine a palpitating sensual life, rich in sensual pleasures and in mutual stimulation and collective security—yet there is something wanting in the corporate life of the ant, all the same, one perceives. In the dangerous situation Derek Wragge Morley describes, it is evident that some general staff work to take hold of, and intellectualize the excitement, and communicate the 'abstract' arrived at to the community, is wanting. To initiate such an activity, a general means of communication would seem to be needed to by-pass such a laborious channel of information as the mutual touching of feelers. The same necessity for generalship seems to brood over the changing of a nest site, or the winter hibernation and the slow and painful re-establishment of the life, trails and food resources of the colony after its winter sleep. The ants lack the instruments of language and record-making without which generalship and planning are impossible. Only through them could the ant colony transcend the time factor and begin that cumulative deepening of experience and understanding which seems to belong even to the most primitive and static human community.

It is probably true that ants are the most successful living land form, apart from man. They have colonized the subsoil the world over. 'There are to-day as you read this 1,280,000,000,000,000 crawling in and around the surface of the earth. The true figure is probably nearer 10,000,000,000,000,000,' Mr. Morley gleefully records.[1] So that the ant cannot be regarded as an obscure by-product of evolution, an off-shoot of the main evolutionary line, but on the contrary, a victory for the Life Force, a

[1] Ibid., p. 175.

world conqueror and world colonizer side by side with man. Yet the ant fumbles around in a sensual darkness just beyond the frontiers of the spiritual dimension, entry into which might assure for it that conquest of the world which science-fiction writers like H. G. Wells chilled our childhoods by imagining.

We see what it really means to take possession of the spiritual dimension if we look at some of the artistic achievements of primitive men, as for example the cave paintings of Lascaux and Altamira, or the contemporary work of bushmen and Australian aborigines. In the long rambling caves of Lascaux in France, photographed and described by Ferdinand Windels[1] with such brilliance, primitive men have left records of the ruminants living in their day which are without parallel for beauty and freshness. Professor Windels recalls that when the first examples of Paleolithic art were discovered and analysed at the beginning of the twentieth century, Reinach and other prehistorians argued that the representations of animals discovered in the caves were totemic in origin. They were symbolic figures which presided over tribal or moiety destinies, and so had been fashioned in the stillness and darkness of the womb-like caves for a deep religious purpose. But this left very much unexplained. To begin with, the Lascaux, the Altamira and most other cave paintings of Europe are realistic, not formal. What one sees on the walls, the author explains, is certainly not the stereotype of an imagined totemic ancestor, half animal, half God or monster, such as we discover for example in Red Indian totemic carvings, but impressionistic portraits of creatures alive and contemporary with the painter. In any case, the primitive artists were extremely selective. In their paintings, ruminants—horse, ox, bison, deer, and ibex for example—abound, but carnivores are missing, birds and plants rare, snakes and tiny creatures almost unknown, and man himself merely a formal pattern unless he too is in some sort of animal disguise. In truth, the caves are portrait galleries of the creatures men hunted.

'It is indeed around hunting that all the interests of Paleo-

[1] *The Lascaux Cave Paintings*, London, 1949.

lithic man are concentrated. The whole life of the tribe depends on the game which he brings home. The meat is used for food; the skins for clothing; needles and awls are made of the bones; the tendons serve for sewing, and also, no doubt, as bindings for the hafting of tools. Horn and antlers are of solid material, but easier to work than stone. The fat is used for lamps. On success in hunting the life of the group depends. But animals are swift and strong creatures; they know how to hide, and to fight. So man tries to conciliate the great unknown forces governing the world. Magic rites are enacted, in the mysterious depths of the caves, by sorcerers. Through their performances, tested by time and thence handed faithfully down the generations, the animals are held bound by magic forces; they will fall victims to every trap, and every dart will kill them. Magic force, too, will ensure the abundance of the game-supply, the reproduction of animals that do man good and the destruction of those that harm him...'[1]

This interpretation seems to-day beyond dispute. Immediately we are impelled to link cave art with the art of the aborigine and the increase ceremonies he performs. How effective the magic proved is not for us to know, but a second and different species of magic is revealed in the paintings and engravings themselves. Whence came that untutored power to render realistically, with pigment on rough rock, the breathing life of the hunted creatures? Man here is engaged in a miracle of creation which could spring only from a further miracle of identification. In order to paint the horse and the plunging deer, he is, for the time, himself the horse and deer. He is wrapt in his subject, living it, seeing it, feeling for its behaviour as the hunter on the plains must do, and with such power there in the dark cave as to bring it to trembling life again before him in the flickering light of lamps of moss and tallow. The spiritual energies directed to the success of hunts yet to be organized have brought forth a creative exploration of the realm most close and vital to man's own life. But, Ferdinand Windels asks, 'can one genuinely maintain that the requirements of magic and the chances of circumstances were the only causes behind the miraculous flowering of

[1] Ibid., pp. 52-5.

Paleolithic art? . . . Surely the admirable friezes of deer and ibexes, or the charming parade of little horses, or harmoniously balanced groups like the black oxen in the Main Chamber or the back-to-back bison in the Nave, could scarcely have been conceived and designed without any sensibility to beauty. . . . And why wish to dissociate magic utility from artistic spontaneity? There is no more incompatibility between them than between religious faith and artistic creation. Who would dream of denying artistic gifts to the Christian primitive . . ?'[1]

The Paleolithic cave artist was every bit as full of hungry vitality as an ant, every whit as sensually excitable. He was a hunter of rapacity and resource, the dreaded contriving enemy of everything that ran on four legs which he could use or eat. I would not wish to reduce in any way the animal stature of this beast of prey. But the same description would serve for the tiger or wolf! Man was also at all times, since his first emergence, more than a hunting animal. His powerful will was more informed about his world than the wills of other creatures, for he was able to range over it in a manner not granted to them. The imaginative reach of his mind—its power of projection—gave him the ability to foresee just in what situation his will might be effective, his longings fulfilled, even if they were only for a full belly, and so to prepare either to meet those situations properly equipped, or even deliberately to bring them about. And it is just because of this gift that he was capable of that imaginative identification with his intended victims which is the source of his cave art. It is not to be supposed that Paleolithic man intellectualized this situation in any manner modern man would understand as scientific. It has been said of primitive man that everything inside him was outside him, and everything outside him was inside him. What appears so often to be an intellectual insight is often an intuitive grasp of the realities of a situation. Early man was not a philosopher, Erich Neumann has said: abstract questions were alien to his consciousness, 'Mythology, however, is the product of the collective unconscious, and anyone acquainted with primitive psychology must stand amazed

[1] Ibid., pp. 64-5.

at the unconscious wisdom which rises up from the depths of the human psyche. . .'[1]

It is of course true that we would condemn much of what Paleolithic man believed as dark and superstitious and no more an account of reality than the night-terrors of a child. Yet that very darkness is more illuminating than much intellectual light would be. Levy-Bruhl has said[2] that 'the primitive makes no distinction between this world and the other, between what is actually present to sense, and what is beyond. He actually dwells with invisible spirits and intangible forces. To him it is these that are the real and actual. His faith is expressed in his most insignificant as well as his most important acts. It impregnates his whole life and conduct.' This was the primitive sense of the sacred about which I wrote in an earlier chapter, and I must once again draw attention to my conclusion there that it reflects not an absurdity in the primitive from which man will presently free himself, but a truth about man which we deny at our peril—that man is saturated with a consciousness of the power of the spiritual within him, and cannot fail to seek to read that element into the world which surrounds him, and that this is one more witness to the separation of man from nature through his entry into the spiritual dimension. It is quite clear that primitive man cannot believe that this spiritual power is not totally effective throughout living nature, and for that matter the dead world too, in just the way that he is forced by intuitive understanding of his own inwardness to believe that it is effective in his own life. All primitive art is a witness to this faith.

However, what I have raised in the short examination of Paleolithic art above is the identification of man the hunter with his prey, an identification so complete as almost to extinguish the ego. The hunter, the 'I', the beneficiary and instigator of all the primitive magic and art, is a mere diagram or cipher on the walls he illuminates like a medieval missal. Now primitive man does not need to make art in order to achieve identification. The

[1] *Origins and History of Consciousness*, 1954, p. 13.
[2] In *Primitive Mentality*, London, 1923, p. 31.

two little hunters I wrote about in *Heron Lake*[1] achieved that without putting paint or pen to paper. But art, or language, or some artifact is necessary to *communicate* the identification, whether that communication is designed simply to inform, or to serve as a spiritual contagion which will call up a similar response in others. Throughout all the activities of man we come face to face with communication by many different instruments. Art is simply one of them. It is no more solitary than language or religion. Art is *above all* communication. It is absurd to imagine that the Paleolithic artist painted or engraved for himself alone. It is probable, on the contrary, that his works of art were undertaken as the peak of some ecstatic increase ceremony, but certainly they were meant for the eyes of other initiates in whom they were intended to rouse the same fierce consciousness of ends to be willed as those which beat in the soul of the artist-priest. Yet they had still another purpose, and that was to influence events externally, to assist in the ordering of the world outside. They were in that sense communications to powers beyond man, intended to set in train causes favourable to man. If I call that power God, perhaps I shall be misunderstood. But one can legitimately speak of gods, and of demonic forces, like the dreadful fears which oppress even the most modern and emancipated childhood, in control of things beyond man, but yet accessible in some manner to man. This second power of communication is not in any sense at war with the powers of identification. As any creative artist knows, the greater the sense of identification with the material, the more luminous the communication.

In earlier chapters I spoke of man's dissatisfaction with nature as he found it. Not even his own body satisfied him and he has both mutilated and decorated it, not simply for aesthetic ends, but for moral and social ones—often precisely to demonstrate that he is not one of the animals. But that dissatisfaction which leads him to creative experiment on his own body, is typical of the whole of his life. He refuses to live as equipped by nature to live: he does not live as a gregarious anthropoid in the forest

---

[1] London, 1948, p. 37.

fringes, but makes over every environment he takes possession of, seeking control of nature or even its entire reshaping in his own interests. This demands of him a highly integrated social life, advanced techniques, a morality objectified in codes and customs like exogamy, and not simply subjectively experienced, and the highly flexible instruments of communication without which these techniques could not be born. Man is a political animal, Aristotle said. He is also a technical one. He is also 'an historical animal, with a deep sense of his own past'. He is all three because he is a spiritual animal. When we range with our imaginations through all the varied social, technical and religious activities of man, we see that nothing in that whole realm is given to man in nature, neither speech nor dances, nor hair-styles, nor clothes, nor flags, nor political systems, nor fire-works, nor organized churches, nor schools, nor newspapers, nor funerals, nor tribal drums. In all that vast realm of purely human activities man has to create his life out of nothing, for nothing natural is given to him, and for what he wants to do he can find no precedents or instructions in nature, not even in the anthill. So true is this that we find out much more about primi-tive man by examining his surviving artifacts than by looking at his fossil bones. There is no natural reason for all this human contriving. But there is a spiritual reason. The myriad human social, political and aesthetic creations are the contrived instru-ments of a spiritual life. They are the forms which belong to history and to cultures, and if man wants to live that life he must fashion what vehicles he can to make it possible, within nature or against nature, or for ever forfeit the hope of it and sink back to an unspeakable natural condition.

It was with the power of communication, and the wish, even the longing, to communicate that I brought the last chapter to an end. Language, I argued, was not purely egocentric: it did not simply fulfil some muscular or intellectual need of the solitary man. To carry the world around in words in the head was not the only, or even the first, purpose of language. Speech was worthless unless it was understood, and the first necessity of speech is to seek a receptive ear. There is always therefore the other side to art and to speech—the listener, who in any case is not going to remain silent, but will give rise to dialogue, to converse; and for just what that can do in the search for and illumination of truth we have the witness of Socrates. The German psychologist Wilhelm Dilthey was perhaps the last great thinker really to explore all the implications of communication. He saw that man is possessed of a peculiar power to re-enact in himself, without confusion of another consciousness with his own, what is taking place in the mind of another. He saw too that this sympathy or *rapport* is somehow fundamental to the human condition. He argued that much of human activity is directed towards deepening the understanding of the contents of consciousnesses other than our own across both time and space—hence history, or the hunger for history, and the development of methods of transpatial communication. The list of the means of communication is inexhaustible. It is possibly all the extravert activities of man, for man communicates what is going on in his mind unconsciously as well as consciously. We reconstruct a culture from shards of coloured pottery, or seek to elucidate the attitude of a tribe towards its members by looking at the vocabulary and syntax of its language; the unconscious revelations of the human condition are in fact greater than the conscious ones in volume, though not in quality. Suffice to say that what is intuitive and accidental in primitive life becomes deliberate and organized in civilized life, which 'takes up' art, literature, music, sculpture and scientific research to enhance human mastery of the spiritual. Indeed, if one pursues the arguments of Wilhelm Dilthey far enough one concludes that the deepening and strengthening of man's spiritual understanding is finally to be regarded as the whole purpose of life—this and not happiness, or success, or scientific knowledge, or utopia. It is not necessary to pursue this important point here, though I believe it to be both true and neglected. What must be said is that what goes on in the spiritual dimension is communicable by art, speech and other artifacts and that this is one of the most important aspects of the life of that dimension. Yet this raises another, and even greater possibility, *that the spiritual realm is itself a communication.*

We certainly have to conclude, if my case is convincing, that entry into the spiritual is an illumination to man of the terms and potentialities of his own mortal life, and that once launched into it he is separated from nature and can in no way return to that state of pristine innocence about the world and about itself which belongs to the animal in nature. Put that way, the entry into the spiritual dimension is a revelation of that which is beyond nature and is pulling man out of it. What is this other, and what is its source? It must be true that it is timeless and spaceless, or it could not achieve for man that limited transcendence of these dimensions which appears to be the mark of his spiritual condition. It can be argued, and of course *is* in many theories of emergence, that in some way the spiritual is brought into existence by the struggles of nature at its mole-like task of thrusting evolution blindly on. If this is true then nature brought into existence that which, by definition almost, is totally unlike itself. The gulf between nature and the realm of the spiritual is greater than that between the inorganic and the organic.

It can be supposed, on the other hand, that man himself has created the realm of the spiritual by efforts of his own. As what the psychologists call man's consciousness dawns, the argument runs, so he begins to understand his condition and to create the realm above nature into which he can venture. Yet it is difficult to accept that man not only forced an entry into this other world but invented it at the same time. That is like arguing that the fish invented the ocean as a place in which to swim. Even to speak of forcing an entry into this realm lands us immediately into difficulties which have been admirably summarized by Erich Neumann:

'However much the world forced early man to face reality, it was with the greatest reluctance that he consciously entered into this reality. Even to-day we can see from primitives that the law of gravity, the inertia of the psyche, the desire to remain unconscious, is a fundamental human trait. Yet even this is a false formulation, since it starts from consciousness as though that were the natural and self-evident thing. But fixation in unconsciousness, the downward drag of its specific gravity, cannot be called a desire to remain unconscious; on the contrary, *that* is the natural thing. There is, as a counter-acting force, the desire to become conscious, a veritable instinct impelling man in this direction. One has no need to desire to remain unconscious; *one is primarily unconscious* and can at most conquer the original situation in which man drowses in the world, drowses in the unconscious, contained in the infinite like a fish in the environing sea. The ascent towards consciousness is the "unnatural" thing in nature; it is specific of the species Man, who on that account has justly styled himself Homo Sapiens. The struggle between the specifically human and the universally natural constitutes the history of man's conscious development.'[1]

This reminds me of Nicholas Berdyaev's epigram: 'Man as we know him is but to a small extent human; he is even inhuman. It is not man who is human, but God. It is God who requires of man that he should be human; man on his part makes very little demand for it.'[2]

This falling back into unconsciousness, into the drowse of Nature, into the forgetfulness which belongs to the natural cycle, tells its own story. Man does not belong *by nature* to the

[1] Op. cit., p. 16. (Italics mine.) More is being said in this than appears on the surface. The true significance of Neumann's summing-up is to be gathered only by examining his technical use of the words *conscious* and *unconscious*, a use which he shares of course with most psychologists. *Any* animal is conscious in the physiological sense. It is only unconscious if asleep, or injured, or drugged in such a manner as to knock out of action its higher centres. *Consciousness* in the technical psychological sense is opposed to the equally technical *unconsciousness*. The latter means psychical processes going on below the threshold of awareness, the former means those which go on above it. But what is awareness? The animal too is aware of its identity and integrity and defends them. Consciousness in the human is a *special* sense of awareness, it is *self*-consciousness, *super*-consciousness, something over and above the animal consciousness. It is this which makes a man aware of moral and intellectual problems, of the struggles of his own psyche for self-realization, or of the tensions of his relationships with nature, with other persons and with the gods, or God. What the psychologist appears to mean by his technical use of the word consciousness is what I mean by spirit. By what I have said of spirit I hope I have shown that it is a less confusing term. However, these reservations do not abate my admiration for Neumann's book and for the struggles of the Jungians in general to elucidate the human situation in spiritual terms.

[2] *The Divine and the Human*, London, 1949, p. 110.

spirit. He is even unhappy there. We witness time and time again in the world the resentment at being human, at shouldering the burdens and responsibilities and moral decisions which go along with humanity, and the longing instead to get away from the human, back into the amoral oblivion of the sensual natural world. And this especially seems to me to be in harmony with the consciousness which we all must have that man is a stranger in the spiritual world, still half at war with it, still exploring it, and even yet does not know the depth or the height or the ultimate power of it. The spiritual realm appears inexhaustible to man, and must really be so, in sharp contrast to the precise limits set to the possibilities open to organisms in the crowded, fully developed realm of living nature in which, we are told, development has ceased.

The truth seems to be that the human entry into the spiritual is a growth in awareness of the ultimate realities of the universe, a growth towards the Godhead. It is the Jacob's ladder held out to man, the opportunity of the divine ascent. Neumann in his *Origins and History of Consciousness* speaks somewhere of how time and again *light* is the central symbol of the creation myths. For him it is a symbol of consciousness: he quotes the Maori text which I have put on the title page, 'The light, the light, the seeking, the searching, in chaos, in chaos.' The more one ponders the mystery of man, the less probable it seems that one misshapen Hominoid blundered into the realm of the specifically human, and the more probable it is that man was *called* into it, or even *commanded* into it, by Divine act. I recognize that this is a view which brings me so close to the doctrine of the special creation of man as to be indistinguishable from it. What seems to me the most appropriate and acceptable explanation of the human condition is *the call* of the Holy Ghost, 'the Lord and Giver of Life'. 'The Dayspring from on high hath visited us,' and man is man because he was summoned out of the world of nature to be man and to worship and to serve God as a free responsible being, and spirit is incarnate in him. To speak of God and man in these terms is perhaps to be excessively theological in a work such as this, true though I believe them to be.

Whether man evolved into the spiritual, or burgled his way into it, or was thrust into it against his will may not matter even theologically compared with the fact that he *is* in it, and has always been in it, and has grown in stature through it. It will be appropriate therefore to conclude by putting the concept of man's call out of nature in the words of Santayana, who described himself as a naturalist and sometimes even thought of himself as a materialist:

'There is accordingly an escape from death open to man; one not found by circumventing nature, but by making use of her own expedients in circumventing her imperfections. Memory, nay, perception itself, is a first stage in this escape, which co-incides with the acquisition and possession of reason. When the meaning of successive perceptions is recovered with the last of them, when a survey is made of objects whose constitutive sensations first arose independently, this synthetic moment contains an object *raised above time on a pedestal of reflection*, a thought indefeasibly true in its ideal deliverance, though of course fleeting in its psychic existence. Existence is essentially temporal and life foredoomed to be mortal, since its basis is a process and an opposition; it floats in the stream of time, never to return, never to be recovered or repossessed. But ever since substance became at some sensitive point intelligent and reflective, ever since time made room and pause for memory, for history, for the consciousness of time, a god, as it were, became incarnate in mortality and some vision of truth, some self-forgetful satisfaction, became a heritage that moment could transmit to moment and man to man. Apprehension, which makes man so like a god, makes him in one respect immortal; it quickens his numbered moments with a vision of what never dies, the truth of those moments and their inalienable values.

'To participate in this vision is to participate at once in humanity and divinity, since all other bonds are material and perishable, but the bond between two thoughts that have grasped the same truth, of two instants that have caught the same beauty, is a spiritual and imperishable bond.'[1]

[1] *The Life of Reason*, Vol. 3. 'Reason in Religion', George Santayana, London, 1905, pp. 262-3. (Italics mine.)

Index